THE SPIRITUAL GUIDE TO MENTAL HEALTH

SAMUEL B. LEE M.D.

www.TheSpiritualPsychiatrist.com
samuelbsleemd@gmail.com

This book is dedicated to my beloved spiritual teacher, Dr. Joseph Michael Levry. I am eternally grateful to him for choosing to incarnate and dedicate his life to the Great Work. I sometimes think about what sacrifices, discipline, and dedication it took for him to develop his consciousness to the point where it is today, and I can only be in wonder and humble gratitude.

I imagine that even in the difficult times during his journey, he felt a deep love for each and every soul that he touched and continued to endure, persevere, and overcome. I like to think that I am one of those souls. Dr. Levry's unconditional love, powerful instruction, unwavering belief, and ability to see only the good in me, even when I couldn't see the good in myself, is the reason why this book has come to fruition.

To find a spiritual teacher of this magnitude is the greatest gift a man can receive on earth. Thank you, Dr. Levry, from my heart. I hope to follow in your footsteps, carry on the Great Work, and open as many hearts as possible while I have the gift of breath.

TABLE OF CONTENTS

Introduction 1

Chapter 1: A Brief Review of the History of Psychiatry 5

Chapter 2: Connection is the Best Medicine 9

   A. Whatever You Are Going Through, Love Is the Answer 9

      Christ Consciousness 10

      Love Cures All Suffering 11

      We Are Never Alone 11

      Connectedness in the Body... 15

      Relationships 16

      The Dis-ease Pyramid Scheme 17

Chapter 3: The Foundation for Health 21

   A. NEWSTART™ 21

      N stands for Nutrition. 21

      E stands for Exercise. 24

      W stands for Water. 25

      S stands for Sunshine.. 26

      T stands for Trust in Higher Self.. 27

      A stands for Air. 29

      R stands for Rest/Sleep... 34

      T stands for Temperance, Discipline, or Self-Control.......... 35

   B. Staple Supplements 36

Chapter 4: Depression.. 37

   A. A Conscious Paradigm of Depression 37

B. My Testimony of Depressive Experiences 43

C. How Western Psychiatry Treats Depression 48

D. Tapering off of Psychiatric Medications 49

E. Natural Alternative Treatments for Depression 50

    Nutritional Psychiatry: Treatments for Depression 50

F. 21-Day Program to Kick Depression 64

Chapter 5: Bipolar Disorder 65

A. A Spiritual Paradigm of Bipolar Disorder 65

B. My Testimony of Manic Experiences 67

C. Western Psychiatry and Bipolar Disorder 70

D. Alternative Treatments for Bipolar Disorder 73

    Diet 73

    Foot Treatments 73

    Breathwork for Bipolar Disorder 74

Chapter 6: Anxiety 75

A. An Energetic Paradigm of Anxiety 75

B. Westernized Perspective of Anxiety: 79

C. Western Treatment of Anxiety 80

D. My Testimony of Anxiety 81

E. Natural Ways to Combat Anxiety 84

    Breathwork 84

    Nutritional Psychiatry for Anxiety 88

    Herbs/Plant Medicine 89

Chapter 7: Psychosis 93

A. A Conscious Paradigm of Psychosis 93

B. Westernized Psychiatry and Psychosis 99

C. Westernized Treatment of Psychosis 101

D. Natural Treatment Approaches Towards Psychosis 101

    Breathwork 101

Nutritional Therapy for Schizophrenia 103

Chapter 8: Alzheimer's Dementia 105

A. A New Paradigm of Alzheimer's 105

B. Current Scientific Paradigm of Alzheimer's Dementia 109

C. Current Westernized Paradigm and Treatment of Alzheimer's ... 111

D. Natural Treatment Approaches for Dementia 112

Kirtan Kriya 112

Supplements and Diet 113

Music Therapy 114

Nutritional Therapy for Alzheimer's 115

Herbs 116

Chapter 9: Attention-Deficit/ Hyperactivity Disorder 117

A. An Energetic Paradigm of ADHD 117

B. Modern Western View and Treatment of ADHD 119

C. Natural Treatment Approaches Towards ADHD 122

Breathwork for ADHD 122

Nutritional Therapy for ADHD 122

Plant Medicine 122

Chapter 10: Addiction 125

A. Addiction from a Spiritual Perspective 125

B. Modern Westernized View and Treatment of Addiction 126

C. Natural Treatment Approaches Towards Addiction 129

Community 129

Cigarette Addiction 129

Opiate Addiction 130

Chapter 11: Post-Traumatic Stress Disorder 133

A. PTSD from a Spiritual Perspective 133

B. Modern Western View and Treatment of PTSD 135

C. Natural Treatments for PTSD 137

    Best Medicine for PTSD 137

    Treatment for Nightmares... 138

    Recommendations for PTSD 138

    Alternative Treatments... 139

Chapter 12: Death and Geriatric Care... 141

    A. A Spiritual Perspective of Death 141

    B. Westernized View and Treatment of Death/End of Life 143

    C. Alternative Approaches Towards End-of-Life Care 145

    Plant Medicine 145

Chapter 13: Miscellaneous Items 147

    A. Couples Counseling 147

    B. How to Safely Taper off of SSRI Medications 148

    C. A Word on Sleep 149

    How to Reprogram Your Subconscious Mind While You Sleep ... 150

    D. Traumatic Brain Injury 150

    E. Making the Unconscious and Subconscious Mind Conscious 151

    Holotropic Breathwork 151

    Resources to Change Your Subconscious Mind 153

Chapter 14: Synchronization, Rhythm, Orchestration – Science Is the Modern Language of Spirituality. Here's Some Science... 155

    Neuroinflammation and Mental Health 155

    The Orchestra of Neurotransmitters 158

    GABA & Serotonin 159

    Detox 160

    Detoxification Support... 161

    Circadian Rhythm 162

    Circadian Rhythm Support 164

    Intermittent fasting, mTOR, and Autophagy 165

Autophagy Support 166

Neurosupport and Neuroprotect 167

About the Author.. 169

Chapter 15: Conclusion 171

A. All Mental Health Conditions Are a Lesson, a Blessing, and an
Opportunity for Growth and Experience 171

B. How to Pull the Mind out of the Body 173

C. For the Advanced Spiritual Seeker Who Desires Rapid Self-
Realization 176

D. My Vision... 182

Acknowledgments.. 185

Bibliography 187

MEDICAL DISCLAIMER

The information provided in this book is not meant to be used, nor should it be used, to diagnose or treat any medical condition.

For diagnosis or treatment of any medical problem, consult your physician. The author of this book is not responsible for any specific health or allergy needs that may require medical supervision. The author of this book is not responsible for any damages or negative consequences from adopting any of the health measures listed in this book.

INTRODUCTION

In my 37 years of life thus far I have experienced almost every psychiatric symptom in the psychiatrist's bible, the *Diagnostic and Statistical Manual of Mental Disorders (DSM)*. I could have been labeled with major depressive disorder with psychotic features, bipolar disorder, post-traumatic stress disorder, schizophrenia, generalized anxiety disorder, social anxiety disorder, alcohol dependence, polysubstance abuse, schizoid personality disorder, etc., and placed on medications that would have alleviated my symptoms temporarily but made it nearly impossible to actually heal the root cause of the symptoms. These medications would end up causing chemical imbalances rather than fixing them. I would also be suffering from a host of side effects, which would shut down my energy centers, also known as chakras. I would not be writing this book, as my creative centers would be numbed or shut down completely. It was part of my dharma in this lifetime to become a psychiatrist, experience all of the diagnoses and symptoms, and then overcome them naturally and now share how I did it and the epiphanies I've had along the way. If I would have followed Western medicine, I would have also likely been placed into inpatient psychiatric hospitals on multiple occasions and would have been traumatized.

The cause of almost every psychiatric symptom or diagnosis does not occur on a physical, or biochemical, level. Although the symptoms manifest on a physical plane and do affect the biochemistry of the body, the root causes of mental health problems occur on an energetic or spiritual level, and in order to cure or overcome these symptoms, we must address the root causes. In this book, I will present a new paradigm of mental health, looking at it from an energetic perspective rather than a westernized approach. Please understand that the word "spiritual" simply means awareness, consciousness, or related to energy. I will also share what I've learned about the psychiatric system in my seven years working as a psychiatrist under the Western model. I attended and completed medical school at Loma Linda University, then did my psychiatry residency at Cedars-Sinai Medical Center in Los Angeles, CA until they shut down their psychiatric residency program. After that, I transferred to the University of Washington in Seattle to complete my final year of psychiatry residency. I then moved to Los Angeles and worked as a geriatric psychiatrist. I was the attending physician at an inpatient geriatric psychiatric hospital for a year and also worked at skilled nursing facilities in the afternoon. I was exposed to the system and saw what was happening to our parents and grandparents. My soul couldn't handle the geriatric system anymore, so I then transferred to outpatient psychiatry for the next three years, working in a classic westernized model of psychiatry. I learned a lot about the system and how it works. It was about this time that I discovered the power of yoga and breathwork and immersed myself into a full-on exploration of all things "spiritual." Again, please note that the word spiritual in this book simply means the science of energy, awareness, and consciousness. And as most of us know, everything is energy. After going to the Amazon jungle, traveling around the world, attending countless seminars, retreats, and yoga studios, listening to podcasts and audiobooks, etc., my intuition told me it was time to leave my job, follow my heart, and share what I had learned. So here I go. Please note that this book is largely written from my experience and opinions based on those experiences. It is not as "scientific" as the *DSM*. I sometimes call myself an experiential psychiatrist because I will hardly recommend or speak about anything that I haven't experienced for myself.

This book is about how I shifted my paradigm to view psychiatric symptoms from an energetic lens. I also write about my opinions on how the westernized model of medicine is set up. I offer some practical tools at the end of each chapter, which I find to be effective for treating and alleviating psychiatric symptoms at the root cause rather than the band-aiding of symptoms.

This book is not meant to replace conventional medical care. Please continue to see your doctor as scheduled for any medical "conditions" you may be experiencing.

CHAPTER 1:
A BRIEF REVIEW OF THE HISTORY
OF PSYCHIATRY

The history of psychiatry is a dark one. The moment that it started to view the human psyche as a body and not a soul it opened itself up to a host of practices that can be considered inhumane. In 1879, in Germany, a man named Wilhelm Wundt, sometimes referred to as the father of psychology, theorized that man was like an animal without a soul, a stimulus-response mechanism who must be molded to fit into society. To this day, psychiatrists create diagnoses that label people with diseases if they do not "fit into society."

Francis Galton developed this theory further into "eugenics," which is a pseudoscience that believed humans could be bred to select for desirable traits and weed out undesirable ones. This pseudoscience rapidly spread across Germany, which led to the term "racial hygiene." Adolf Hitler used these concepts and referred to them in his book *Mein Kampf*. This led to the "law of prevention of genetically diseased offspring," which encouraged the eradication of any "diseased" or "weak" offspring. This led to the sterilization of 400,000 Germans over a period of 12 years. This practice led to the opening of 31 psychiatric centers that would murder young children who were born "unfit," with "mercy killings" of "feebleminded people." Medical facilities were turned into gas chambers. Many people were murdered. This practice then evolved into the Holocaust, where millions of people were mass murdered.

Then as "science" started experimenting with humans, psychiatrists began to use an "ice pick" to perform "psychosurgery." They would take out the frontal lobes in "psychotic" patients, believing they had cured them. I am convinced that in a few decades people will look back at current psychiatric medications and realize that psychiatrists were chemically lobotomizing their patients or shutting down/numbing down their frontal lobes.

Point being, when the practice of psychiatry negates the value of each person as a unique soul, this leads to practices that are inhumane and contribute to mass injustices and tragedies, such as the Holocaust. This way of viewing mental illness has led to an evolution of a host of psychiatric diagnoses that continues to grow every time the psychiatrist's bible, also known as the *Diagnostic and Statistical Manual of Mental Disorders* (now in its 5th edition) is revised. We are at a point where every person in society can be labeled with psychiatric diagnoses. These labels and diagnoses are coming from the minds of psychiatrists who are creating these diagnoses based upon research papers, which are often unreliable. Psychiatrists will often admit that there is no validity or reliability to the way the system works. The medications currently being used often shut down the energy centers in the body and numb people to their creativity and joy. It is important to note that psychiatric symptoms often present themselves as warning signs that something needs to be addressed in the person's life. The medications can numb the symptoms but never actually treats the root cause of what's presenting. Thus, the person on medications, though able to stay numb and function temporarily in society, will not be able to address the root cause of what's going on, as they are unaware of what it actually takes to treat the root cause. Thus, the symptoms will continue to reoccur cyclically, the medications will stop working as tolerance is built, and the person eventually will not be able to function at all without psychiatric medications, thus reinforcing the system and those benefiting at the top of the system. It is a system that does not cure but guesses, band-aids, and gets people into a cyclical pattern of more medications, side effects, and hospitalizations. It is also a system that gives no attention to the fact that human beings are, in truth, unique, vibrant, powerful, and creative souls who were not designed to "fit in" to society but to stand out.

Today the practice of categorizing, labeling, locking up, and ostracizing psychiatric patients continues to happen. Psychiatry patients are seen as "unfit" in society and labeled and placed on medications that numb the frontal lobes. However, people are starting to wake up to the idea that there are natural ways to treat mental illness. We are starting to see the human being not as a mechanical instrument but a highly intelligent, unique reflection of Source, God, Allah, Creator, Spirit, Universe—whatever term resonates with you.

The aim of this book is to provide an alternative way of looking at mental illness and to plant seeds that help us see mental illness not as a disease or problem but as a lesson, blessing, and an opportunity for growth. It is my hope that we can shift our paradigms beyond the system and see each other and ourselves from the perspective of the conscious soul. **The main objective of this book is also to provide practical tools, herbs, supplements, and natural modalities of healing that empower the reader to treat the root cause of the symptoms rather than band-aiding symptoms.**

Please keep in mind that the "Spirit" world does not care about our money, comfort, materialism, capitalism, race, sex, societal status, "death," etc. What the Spirit world cares about is our merging with the best version of our Selves. For such a time as this, a spiritual revolution of consciousness is needed so that each person can individually realize their own Christ consciousness (unity mindset that is within each person) so that we can cooperate to help Mother Earth and each other save our planet from further density and chaos. In order to do this, we need the right tools that guide us into our own hearts so that we can realize our own unique individual purposes and then start creating an energy inspired by our hearts to contribute to the Whole. We already have all the necessary technology and resources. All we need now is an increase in global consciousness. This is already happening, and we are infinitely supported in this effort.

Chapter 2:
Connection is the Best Medicine

A. Whatever You Are Going Through, Love Is the Answer

Love is the cohesive power of the Universe and the best medicine for any health problem. The cure for every psychiatric condition is connection, which modern society calls love. Love is the cohesive power of the Universe. It is the glue that connects and holds together every person, family, relationship, atom, and the entire Universe. Without love, people and things fall apart. Life does not make sense without love. The cause of suicidal ideation and addiction is a lack of love. When a person does not have love, they have no purpose, meaning, or reason to get up in the morning, and thus become self-destructive.

Whether we are aware of it or not, there is a micro-intention behind every single thing a person does, and it is either love or selfishness. Love comes from the heart and is the *why* behind the *what*. Without love, the world does not make sense, and there is no purpose or meaning. A suicidal patient is simply a patient who has lost all love in his life and has no reason, no purpose, to keep on going.

A lack of love leads to the opposite of connection, which is fear. Fear leads to separation and isolation, resulting in inflammation. Inflammation leads to dis-ease.

Love is the force which is able to perceive beyond race, sex, gender, or socioeconomic status and see that everything is energy and that we all come from the same Source of energy, breathe the same air, live on the same planet, and are in this Divine dance together as one species. Love is the force that is able to cover over, or negate, a multitude of "sins" (an archery term which simply means "missing the mark," which we were born to do, though the church has mistakenly redefined this to mean "lacking") and cover us with grace. Love holds no record of wrong. So, when we miss the mark, as humans often do, love covers over it, as if we are still imperfectly perfect.

Christ Consciousness

Love connects, unites, forgives, strengthens, and gives you the courage to face any problem. Love never fails. Whatever mental health problem one is going through, the answer is to throw some love at it right now.

The greatest sages and teachers of the past are testaments to the power of love. Jesus performed all of his miracles through the power of love. The electromagnetic energy of love radiating from his heart was so powerful that he could simply look at a stranger with the eyes of love, read into his soul, and speak, "follow me," and they would leave everything behind to follow him because of the love they felt emanating from his heart and aura. This is the power of love. Christ consciousness is not about one man but about a highly advanced technological consciousness, which is available to every man. The basis of this type of consciousness is unconditional love, which allows one to be covered by the grace of love at all times. This consciousness allows one to be liberated upon experience. Even when the person is in the middle of the worst act ever, Christ consciousness allows one to know that even in that moment, love holds no record of wrong, and even while one was committing the most heinous act, they were already, "forgiven." Even in that moment there was abundant grace because even that heinous act is a process in the liberation of that person's and the collective soul. There was no need to have to pay tithe, do penance, say Hail Marys, or do any religious act to be "good enough." The Bible says,

10

"While we were still in our 'sins,' Christ died for us." Even when we were at our worst, love won and will always win.

Love Cures All Suffering

From an energetic standpoint, this means that the higher vibration of love will always entrain any lower vibration, making the ultimate outcome inevitable. We are all born for one reason: to learn how to receive, share, and give love.

When someone is anxious, depressed, or even schizophrenic, if they have abundant connection and love in their lives, they will be able to make it through whatever they are going through. For example, an autistic child with a fiercely loving parent will be able to survive and sometimes even thrive because of love. Love is the best medicine. I have witnessed severely depressed and suicidal patients cured in one moment as soon as they "fall in love." As soon as one experiences true love, the programmed, subconscious, depressive beliefs that were running the show shift to the conscious realization of deep purpose and meaning found in love, and the depression lifts in an instant.

It is important to realize that the belief in lack is the root cause of all suffering. As soon as anyone believes that they lack, they suffer. For example, an autistic child does not know what he lacks, so in his mind, it is not likely he is suffering. It is usually the family member who thinks something is wrong, that it shouldn't be this way, that there is lack, and therefore suffering.

We Are Never Alone

It is important to realize that all of nature is connected through this force of love and that nature is a cohesive, highly interdependent super organism. Everything is interconnected and interdependent with each other. I first experienced this phenomenon during my first ayahuasca ceremony when I was drawn to touch and breathe with a tree. Although I was conscious, I was not in thought and was just naturally allowing my intuition and psyche to move and feel and breathe. At that moment, I remember seeing a multitude of neon green lines coming out of me, into the tree, from the tree, into all of the forest. Imagine that... This neon green, highly interconnected matrix of a spider web connected all parts of nature together through these energetic vibrations, which became visible under the influence of the sacred plant ayahuasca. All of nature was interconnected by these energetic lines. My soul realized at that moment that everything literally is connected and that we are never alone. We all come from the same source, breathe the same air, drink the same water, and live on the same earth. Consciousness is alive, connected, and everywhere. It is often referred to as the one mind. And it is this mysterious force, which we call love, that the Great Architect of the Universe designed to hold us all together. It is my hypothesis that within this energy we call life force, prana, or chi is contained the cohesive power of the Universe. We come to life with our first breath, and it is the last thing that leaves us before we die. Our body returns to the ground, but our Spirit returns to Source. Therefore, within the breath, also referred to as life force, is not only oxygen and energy but also an infinite substance some scientists are starting to call the God particle. It is the cohesive power of the Universe. It is what invisibly holds all things together. It is what gives life. That is why in this book I will focus on the breath as the main instrument we can use to raise awareness, consciousness, and remember who we are. Breath is the movement of Spirit within the body, and when we focus on it, it connects us with our Spirit and helps us activate the biological remembrance of who We really are beyond the ego. If one can learn how to work with the breath of life, any disease is preventable, curable, and all things are possible. Where there is an abundance of prana, no disease can remain.

When one is able to quiet the mind by focusing on the movement of breath within the body, while focusing the physical eyes on the spiritual eye (third eye/pineal gland, aka first eye, aka Ajna chakra), the awareness will enter into the quantum field of cohesiveness and emptiness. There one will easily be able to know that all of what we see comes from one Seed, one Source, and that we are all one. As one focuses on Source and the movement of breath within the body, the ego identity of self, separation, and fear will melt away and blend into the perspective that God is One and in All and that the Christ consciousness lives within each being and is waiting to be unveiled by peeling back the layers of conditioning and programming that hinder it from coming to life on this physical plane. Once the being starts to see God in everything and everyone, the bliss body will activate and the energy of fear, which causes separation, will fall apart. Not only is this true Universally but also within the anatomy of a human being.

The ego self, or lower self, adheres to a belief system of separation; it believes that it is a separate identity from All that is and therefore constantly needs to defend and protect itself. This belief system leads to the collective consciousness of a highly individualized society, which leads to isolation, racism, socioeconomic classes, and disease. Highly evolved energetic beings have been able to completely see through the illusion and attach solely to their Higher Self. The Higher Self naturally understands that they are connected and one with All that is. That separation and fear is simply an illusion of the lower self. Enlightenment simply means all conditioning of separation has been deprogrammed. At this stage, the person engages life unattached to the body, the lower self, and only from a vibration resonating from their Higher Self. Please note that in this book the name Jesus or Higher Self simply refers to the consciousness that has merged with Source and is free from all conditioning. Feel free to substitute the word Source with unconditional love, Mother Mary, or whatever word evokes the consciousness of enlightenment and pure love for you.

Jesus' mind had been healed of all duality. So, in the presence of a leper he did not believe in the ultimate reality of leprosy, and because all minds are connected, the leper in the presence of Jesus also did not believe in the reality of the disease and therefore was healed. There is only one mind, and they are all connected. This is the science of miracles. For example, when Jesus was in the presence of a blind person, He was able to see through the illusion of disease and view the person as whole and complete. He was only engaging the other person's Higher Self, who is already complete, healed, and whole. Science is slowly discovering that all minds are connected and that universally there is one mind. (Please read Larry Dossey's book *One Mind* for more information on this.)

Jesus was able to look beyond the conditioning of sickness to see the person as already whole. Because of all the miracles that were performed, the seeker naturally had faith and belief that they could be made whole by the power emanating from Source in the presence of Jesus. Because all minds are connected, this unique combination of faith, non-duality, and connected minds automatically changed the leper's and blind man's perspectives about their diseases. In Jesus' presence, they also, through faith, were able to see through the illusion of disease, and as they changed their minds about their diseases, the illusions melted away and the leper and blind man were restored to their belief systems. Thus, Jesus is often quoted as saying, "According to your faith, be it unto you." This is the science of miracles. When one can change their mind and belief system beyond the conditioning of the global consciousness of disease or threat and see that the only thing that is real is love, then all illusions will melt away through faith. Only what one believes is real is real. Please understand that Jesus is only one example of a human who was able to obtain a highly evolved consciousness and completely merge with His Higher Self. In fact, there is no difference between Jesus or any other highly evolved being when it comes to the realm of consciousness. Jesus, Hanuman, Krishna, and Allah are all one, as they obtained a consciousness of merging with All that is and with their Higher Self. This means, on a consciousness level, that when one merges with the Higher Self, the boundaries of religion, class, race, and socioeconomic status all melt away. It means someone has been able to deprogram all the conditioning of the mind and completely merge into his or her own Christhood, which lies within each person.

Jesus, however, was unique in that he not only merged with his Higher Self but also proved through the physical crucifixion and resurrection that death does not exist and that the body is only a container for Spirit. He was not attached to His body; thus, he was able to be crucified and prove that the Soul never dies and that the energy of unconditional love prevails over death. For more in-depth, scientific information, please attend one of Dr. Joe Dispenza's seminars or read his book *Becoming Supernatural.*

Connectedness in the Body

At some point in everyone's spiritual journey, they will come to the understanding that all things are connected. This interconnectedness includes the neurotransmitter network in the body. It is my theory that serotonin affects dopamine, which affects norepinephrine, etc. Or, on an organ level, the kidney supports the liver, which supports the heart, etc. So, in some forms of acupuncture, when you want to heal the liver, you actually treat the supporting organ first.

Unfortunately, modern Western science has tried to make human beings into linear objects, which can be manipulated by adjusting one neurotransmitter. What westernized psychiatry fails to understand is that when you change the levels of one neurotransmitter, such as serotonin, it affects the balance of every other neurotransmitter and organ that is connected upstream or downstream. All of nature, including humans, is highly interdependent upon one another. And as is within, so is without. As is above, so is below. Altering the levels of one neurotransmitter, though a particular symptom may improve temporarily, does nothing to cure the actual cause of the symptom, which is linked to an energetic problem in the unseen world rather than a physical manifestation in the seen world. What we see is about 1% of reality. It is the unseen world that controls or manifests into the seen world. For example, unseen belief systems produce unseen thoughts, which produce unseen emotions, which then vibrate into each cell, affecting cell permeability and the instructions to the genes on which proteins and hormones to code for, etc. Therefore, the use of most Western psychiatric medications, though they can lead to a temporary relief of symptoms by altering the levels of one neurotransmitter, over the course of a long period of time, actually cause a chemical imbalance by disturbing the nature of the neurotransmitters, their receptors, and all that is connected to them. By changing the levels of serotonin by taking a pill formulated in a lab, my belief is that in the long term this not only causes an "imbalance" of the receptors for serotonin but also everything connected to them, which is every other neurotransmitter, tissue, and organ, including the brain.

Relationships

It has been said that when "I" is replaced by "WE," "Illness" becomes "WEllness." Many research studies have consistently shown that the number-one factor that determines happiness and contentment with one's life is the quality of connection and support one feels from their loved ones and community.

When I was working in the skilled nursing facility system for a year, it was evident which residents had invested in relationships and which ones had invested in money or the accumulation of material possessions. Those who had invested in relationships were happier, brighter, and had people visiting them regularly. You could literally see the sparkle in their eyes, which ancient Buddhists knew is connected with the heart via energy channels—thus the saying, "the eyes are the window to the soul." They possessed a warm glow and sense of connectivity, even those who were suffering from "dementia." Those who had invested their lives in money or resources were usually left isolated, with emptiness in their eyes and their life savings now being depleted to pay for their geriatric care.

There is a child in a third-world country who has absolutely nothing to his name but has a loving family and can be found running around in a field with childlike joy. On the other hand, there is a famous actor who has everything a man could desire in the world but feels completely empty, isolated, and miserable. The child has love in his life and thus feels no lack, while the actor, though having it all when it comes to material possessions, lacks love and connection and therefore is miserable. Jesus said, "What does a man gain if he gains the whole world but loses his own soul?"

True, heartfelt connection to oneself and then to others is the best medicine for any dis-ease. And love is the power that connects. It is the power that holds together our atoms, cells, tissues, organs, marriages, families, communities, and our Universe. It is the ultimate medicine for all conditions. The world is literally dying from a starvation of love. Unfortunately, most Western intellectuals believe only in what science can prove in a lab, therefore eliminating the concept of the soul and of love.

The Dis-ease Pyramid Scheme

Many mental health practitioners label a patient into a category and promote the idea that the person has a "chemical imbalance in the brain." This leads to a sense of lack or suffering in the person, which leads to a false belief, false emotions, and the resulting coding of the genes, which produces neuropeptides and hormones that are in alignment with the false belief the pharmaceutical companies are spreading and advertising. **The belief in lack is the cause of all suffering.** As soon as one believes they have a chemical imbalance, it actually starts to cause one. The belief leads to a feeling, which leads to a vibration in the body and cells, which leads to a change in cell permeability and the coding of genes for hormones and proteins, which are in alignment with the person's core belief that there is something wrong with them. This leads to further reinforce the belief that they are not good enough, need to be fixed, and don't fit in. This leads to isolation, which leads to a lack of love and connection, which leads to inflammation and dis-ease. Isolation causes inflammation, which causes all disease. The current Western mental health system is propagating a belief that if people have certain symptoms, then they have a corresponding chemical imbalance, which leads them to seek medication from a psychiatrist, which benefits the pharmaceutical companies and those at the top of the pyramid scheme. The medications that are dispensed do not treat the core cause of the symptoms but only seek to temporarily disturb the level of neurotransmitters long enough so the patient can feel numb enough to function in the same society and environment, which likely is causing the symptoms. Thus, the condition is never cured but temporarily band-aided until a higher dose and other medications are needed, thus continuing to benefit those at the top of the pyramid scheme. **A cure or treating the root cause does not make money**. And then, when those at the top of the pyramid scheme make the money, the greed and lust for more money is never satisfied, and more schemes are slowly infused into the system from the top down while the patient continues to suffer.

When the body starts making proteins and hormones that make the person feel separate and different because of a diagnosis, the person further starts to feel that they do not fit in and are damaged and continue to isolate and experience low-vibration emotions chronically. This further propagates the condition, leading to all kinds of diseases, such as cancer.

What is truly needed is a sense of connection and a supportive community that holds space for the patient to go through their process without labeling them or trying to fix them like they need to be repaired. An ideal community would be one that chooses to connect and unconditionally hold space for the patient despite their symptoms. When a patient has a supportive community and loving mentors, they can maintain a sense of hope, faith, and love internally while continuing to face whatever may be going on externally, all the while knowing that whatever is happening is going to help them evolve. Mental health challenges are not a disease but a lesson, blessing, and opportunity for growth. And whatever the person overcomes, they now have the keys to the consciousness or moral authority to help others overcome. This is why love is the best medicine. With love and connection to a supportive community and mentors, you can endure and conquer any challenge. Love is the most powerful force in the world, and each person has an endless reservoir in his or her heart. Love is limitless. The more you give, the more is returned. There is no end to the eternal river of life and love flowing from the heart. The Universal rule is that the energy that you give is equal to the energy that comes back to you. The law of attraction is based upon this Universal law, as is the law of cause and effect, also sometimes referred to as karma.

The actual cause of most mental health conditions can be traced back to continuously ignoring the energetic GPS system of the body, the heart. The heart is the seat of the soul and where intuitive intelligence lives. The heart will never lead you astray if you listen to it. The electromagnetic field the heart generates is at least 5 to 15 times as radiant as the field the brain creates. The Heart-Math Institute has been conducting groundbreaking research that scientifically proves the miraculous intelligence of the heart. It is constantly monitoring all of the systems of the body and changing the variability of the body's rhythm to give the it exactly what it needs in that moment. If you pay attention to it, and listen to it, it will guide you to your purpose, your meaning, your North Star and activate your bliss body, which is your birthright. The heart is a magnet; if you follow it, it will not lead you astray. It will not only reveal your deep purpose for incarnating but also attract everything you need along the way. Your heart will not fail you because love never fails. **The reason for most mental health problems, as well as the reason that heart disease is the number one cause of death in America, is partially due to diet and physical reasons but mainly because we are listening to our analytical minds and neglecting our hearts**. The heart on an energetic level is "dying" because of a lack of paying loving attention to it and listening to it. Where attention goes, blood flows, and it grows. Most of society spends all day listening to their brains, which 95% of the time are focused on a past thought or future anxiety. When was the last time we stopped to simply pay attention to our hearts, nonetheless listen to them? This takes practice. The voice of the mind is noisy, but the voice of the heart is a soft knowing.

The problem is that most people are so busy unconsciously listening to and paying attention to the noise in their minds that they either ignore the heart or miss its promptings. For example, one may find that she is continuously going to a job that she knows deep in her heart is not the right job for her. Or one may find that he is in a relationship that deep down his heart knows is not right. However, because of the pressure of society and widespread belief in the importance of money, having a job, paying off bills, needing someone else to be complete, etc., these people continue to ignore the voices of their hearts and go to this job or stay in this relationship that no longer serves them. At first, the voice of the heart is strong; however, once it is continuously ignored, the voice became quieter until it is mute. Then the process of going into a job that does not promotes one's happiness takes a toll and leads to daily stress, inflammation, then symptoms such as depression, anxiety, etc.

Quiet the mind, and the heart will speak. In order to quiet the mind, one must enter into a state of internal peace. This is most rapidly established by allowing the breath to lead the mind into stillness. Silence is audible sound, and this is where we can hear the voice of the heart, also known as intuition. By finding a rhythmic breathing pattern, the brain waves will entrain to the rhythm of the breath, and the heart will start beating in coherence to the rhythm of the breath and brain waves. This will allow one to find calm abiding and to listen to the voice or intelligence of the heart. The voice of the heart is not usually an audible voice but an inner knowing. This is the sixth sense of intuition, which knows what is best even before the event has occurred. Therefore, it is vital that each person spend time getting to know the Divine intelligence and spiritual GPS system that is alive within the heart. It will not lead you astray. To know your heart is to love your heart. To know something, we must spend time with it. Once we know it, we will trust it. Once we trust it, we will listen to it. When we are in tune with our hearts, it will lead us out of whatever suffering our conditioned minds have led us into.

Love and connection are the best medicines for any mental health problem. Love is the secret sauce in life that will connect the dots and make sense out of life. Therefore, finding a like-minded community that accepts and appreciates your uniqueness would be the first step to health in any mental health situation. Once this has been established, we can focus on the acronym NEWSTART™.

CHAPTER 3:
THE FOUNDATION FOR HEALTH

A. NEWSTART™

Whatever mental health problem is going on, be assured that nature has the answer. **NEWSTART™ is an acronym that symbolizes the foundation, the starting point, for health.** Any health problem can be approached by starting with the fundamental building blocks of nutrition, exercise, water, sunshine, trust in Self, air, rest, and temperance (Newstart Lifestyle Program, 2019). You can find the NEWSTART™ program at www.newstart.com.

N stands for Nutrition.

We are what we eat. Hippocrates said, "Let food be thy medicine and medicine thy food." What we eat becomes the building blocks for our cells, muscles, tissues, organs, brain, thoughts, and energetic body, as they are all connected. With all of the fad diets these days, it is important to realize that no two bodies are alike. Everybody is different. Which means each body has a unique dietary regimen that matches the unique body's needs. This means that one must learn how to listen to their body. Most of society wants a scripted formula to follow and to be told what to do, what to eat, what to say, etc. However, we are entering a period in conscious evolution where listening to your own body's innate wisdom is essential. For some people, meat will be good; for some, it will not.

The foods we eat are the energetic vibratory building blocks our bodies need, and by listening to your own body's innate wisdom, you can discover what type of diet works best for your own body. In Ayurveda, it is widely known that each body has different elemental needs, and the goal is to be in balance with all elements. This means that if the body is "hot" type, then eating more "cooling" foods would be beneficial. Those who want to develop more mental focus, lose weight, and build lean bodies may be drawn to a ketogenic diet. The point being: you have to listen to your own bodies needs and feed it accordingly.

One basic principle for all when it comes to nutrition is to eat whole foods that are in season. Nature is intelligent, and whoever designed nature is also intelligent. Foods that come from the earth in their whole form are more beneficial than just eating separate parts of nature that have been manipulated. Scientists manipulate foods and change them in a lab; take GMO foods, for example. Eating food that has been manipulated is not as beneficial as eating the whole, unaltered plant, vegetable or fruit. The Great Architect of the Universe created food in its whole form for a specific reason. When the whole plant is consumed, it offers a higher alchemical, nutritious value to the body. Another guideline is to pick your foods according to the seasons. If you eat meat, check to make sure the meat is coming from a clean source where the animals are treated with care and without antibiotics. Or else, you may not only be ingesting the meat but also the antibiotics, pesticides, and chemicals released into the meat when the animal was slaughtered. Know where your food comes from, eat whole foods as much as possible, and listen to your body and adjust your diet according to its needs.

Some doctors say that we need to clean the body before we can repair it. Finding a good functional medicine doctor who is well informed on the body's dietary needs may be a good first step to finding what works for your body.

Adjusting your diet is always a good first step in achieving optimal health. This is not only true for the physical benefits but also the mental benefits. Jesus' first temptation after fasting for 40 days was food. Food addiction is real. In fact, sugar addiction is the number one addiction in the world. Many food distributors and fast food chains purposefully put chemicals into the food that make it addictive. When you find the diet that works for you and consistently adhere to it, it will not only help you physically but also on an emotional/mental level. If you have self-discipline when it comes to food, it will carry over to all areas of your life.

Please also note that it's not only about what type of food you eat but what emotional state you are in when you eat. When you are in a rush, the sympathetic nervous system is activated, and you will not absorb the same nutrients as you would when you are in calm parasympathetic state. So, it doesn't matter if you are eating the most expensive spirulina in the world; if you are in a rush, you will be in sympathetic arousal, and the nutrients won't be properly absorbed. The energy of the food will also take on the energy of the emotions at the time of consumption. Therefore, it is always a good practice to form the habit of taking three slow, relaxed breaths before eating, entering a parasympathetic state, and blessing the food you are about to eat. Eating in a state of gratitude is always best, for then you automatically merge with your Higher Self and enter a state of receptivity.

It is also vital to remember by whom and how your food was prepared. Have you ever eaten a home-cooked meal by a mother or grandmother who puts a tremendous amount of love into her cooking? You can literally taste the "love" that was transferred into the food. Therefore, when seeking out sources of regular consumption of food, you want to select food that has been prepared with loving intention and by the hands of someone you trust.

One of the best practices that we can adopt in our daily lives is the practice of **intermittent fasting.** This means that there is a 9 to 12-hour window during the day where food is consumed and a 12 to15-hour window where nothing but water is consumed. Although most of the studies have been done on rats, and show numerous health benefits, one can easily feel the benefits of this practice by simply trying it for three days. You will feel more energy physically, clearer mentally, and "lighter." If practiced consistently, you will find that your body will naturally use fat for energy, which will lead to less fat and more muscle mass. Our ancestors were used to only eating one to two times per day—they did not eat three meals a day! The first few days of intermittent fasting may be difficult, as we have a mental, societally conditioned addiction to food. However, once you flow into a routine of restricting food intake to an ideal nine-hour window, you will soon become addicted to feeling good! It is a sure way to feel more mentally clear and have more energy, which translate to more focus and concentration on your creative flow by which you can help the world become a better place through your creative process.

From an energetic perspective, food is for energy, prana, or life force. Everything is energy. Without energy we can't do anything. To optimize the pranic body, it is vital to eat foods that are alive and contain prana. Most foods even in health stores these days do not contain high prana.

Dr. Dean Ornish has a great dietary regimen which is well researched and beneficial to most human beings. I encourage you to check out his website at www.ornish.com/proven-program/nutrition.

E stands for Exercise.

Movement is life. When we do not move, the internal waters (we are made of at least 75% water) become stagnant, lifeless, and rot. As we move, breathe, and exercise, the internal waters also move and become fresh with life-giving prana. This means stretching and clearing the energy channels known as meridians so that energy can move through our bodies without becoming stuck. Exercise usually involves rhythmic breathing. Every time we breathe properly, the diaphragm moves and stimulates the internal waters while simultaneously giving our organs a free massage. If you ever find yourself depressed or anxious, stop and go exercise for 30 minutes. You'll never find anyone after 30 minutes of swimming pop out of the pool and say, "I'm depressed." You'll never find anyone after running on the beach for 30 minutes say, "I'm anxious." This is because they have changed their energetic levels simply by moving and breathing rhythmically. So, if you find yourself stuck in your mind, thinking low-vibration-energy thoughts, go exercise for 30 minutes. The way you think about yourself and your situation will completely change to the energetic frequency you are vibrating at after your exercise session. It is recommended that you exercise for at least 30 minutes, three times a week, and it is highly recommended you find a form of exercise that involves rhythmic breathing such as yoga, swimming, running, etc.

W stands for Water.

Water is life. We are made of at least 70% water. Let that statement sink in. It is vital that we drink enough water. The first step to health is to become adequately hydrated. Most humans need approximately 6 to 10 cups per day, depending on each individual's needs. Water is the purest element. In modern society, we invest so much energy and money into our foods that we often times forget that water is even more important. We can live over a month without food but less than week without water.

Water can store energy and memories (Emoto, 2005). This means that we can charge our water with the type of energy we want it to have! Water, when frozen and looked at under a microscope, will take on crystallized structures of the energy that it was charged with. This means that if we want to be happy, we should be charging our water with happy words, emotions, music, and energy. The water will store the energy of the music and words, and when we drink the water, the energy will become a part of us. If you decide to invest in something worthwhile, let it be your water. Make sure it comes from a clean source. Fresh spring water is the best, even better than alkalinized, "purified" water. Once again, nature is the best medicine, and spring water bottled at the source is the best water we can drink. Ensure that it is clear and charged with the energy, oxygen, and alkalinity that your body and mind desires.

Another important point to keep in mind is the energetic, emotional state of the person when he/she drinks the water (like with eating food). It doesn't matter how amazing the water is if the person drinking it is in a rush or a state of low-vibration emotions when drinking the water. As soon as the water enters the body, the emotional vibration of the person will be transferred to the water molecules, which then will be diffused into the kidneys and every other organ. Therefore, it is vital that before eating or drinking water, that one pauses, gets into a positive state of being, and then drinks the water. This way the water will be charged with the emotional resonance of the person drinking it. So please slow down, find gratitude, then drink. Water is life. Water is the purest element we have, and we are water.

A good practice to adopt before drinking water is to simply pause, take a deep breath, and visualize something that makes you feel happy or get into a state of gratitude, and say out loud, "Water is life." Hold the water with your hands and visualize the energy being transferred into the water, then drink.

One of the best health practices one can adopt is the practice of drinking warm to hot water with half an organic lemon squeezed into it. Lemon juice acts as a digestive and a detoxifying agent and helps in cleaning the liver, leading to better digestive health. Lemon juice is also an effective way to reduce weight, as it increases the body's metabolic rate. Drinking lemon juice with warm to hot water every morning helps in maintaining the pH balance of the body. The drinking of the hot water is ancient health practice, which science will soon be discovering has numerous health benefits and is good for the liver as well as the killing of harmful agents within the body. There are master yogis who have an intimate connection with the invisible world who are quoted as stating that drinking hot water is one of the best health practices for the liver. There are deep spiritual reasons for this, which you can research if you are interested. However, don't just take my word for it; adopt the practice of drinking a big cup of hot water upon awakening with lemon juice and see what happens.

S stands for Sunshine.

Working with the sun is one of the most powerful energetic practices known to man. The sun is a symbol of unconditional, unchanging, consistent love. It is what gives life to the entire planet. It faithfully rises each morning no matter what you did the night before, bringing the same light to each and every soul without bias or prejudice. It is a symbol of life and love. The sun's life-giving rays will revitalize you with vitamin D, melanin for your skin, and prana. Researchers are slowly becoming aware of how vital melanin can be for one's health. Please don't believe me; do your own research. Sun gazing during the golden hours—within the hour of the sun rising and the hour prior to the sun setting—will activate your pineal gland and regulate your sleep/wake cycles. Jesus said, "...the light of the body is the eye. If therefore thine eye be single thy whole body shall be full of light..." Scholars believe he was referring to the third eye, also called the first eye, which is the ajna chakra located in between the eyes in the middle of the forehead. Working with the sun will activate the third eye and give you a clear and open signal and communication with the divine plane. As the pineal gland becomes in tune with the divine plane, it will regulate the pituitary gland, which will then regulate all of the hormones in the body, and the whole body will be in sync, in rhythm, or as Jesus said, "full of light." Science will forever be revealing the benefits of working with the sun. The science of the sun is beyond what current westernized medicine can even begin to fathom. It is recommended that each individual work with the sun by gazing at it at daily while it is rising with pure intentions and rhythmic breath. This will lead to an improved mood, clearer cognition, boosted energy, and better sleep. This practice is especially important for those who suffer from seasonal affective disorder or become depressed during the winter seasons.

T stands for Trust in Higher Self.

Self-realization is the greatest gift one can give to him/herself or to the planet. To realize who you are on the inside, you must learn how to quiet the mind and listen to your heart while in silence. Silence is inaudible sound. To trust your Higher Self, you must know your Self. To know your Self, you must spend time with your Self. I'm not referring to the ego self but to the intuitive Self, which is revealed in silence, meditation, or prayer. The more time you spend in silence, meditation, and prayer, the more your intuition will increase. Intuition is the sixth sense; it is knowing what is going to happen before it does. If your intuition is heightened, you cannot go the wrong way in life. Spending time in meditation, reflection, and prayer will also start to cleanse the garbage out of your subconscious mind. All of the limiting beliefs, religious programming, and ancestral karma will slowly start to reveal itself to you, at which point, you can then choose a new belief system to serve you for this incarnation or even choose to not abide a particular belief system; you can choose to dwell in the present moment in full and complete trust in the Universe because you have spent time getting to know it and you can let go.

Awareness is the first step of change. So, it is highly recommended that you spend time in silence each day, listening to your internal guidance system and cleansing out the subconscious programming which no longer serves you. Please remember that intention is everything. Intentions stem from deep down in the heart. They are the why behind the what. For everything you say or do, there is always a micro-intention behind it. It is important to get very clear on what you want so that you can set your micro-intention to be in alignment with your heart's desire.

Scientific research shows that two people can perform the exact same task, but the person who understands and knows why they are doing it will have purpose, renewed energy, and a meaning and intention behind what they are doing. This will change the entire energy of the action one is undertaking. Two doctors can give the same treatment; however, the one who has a loving intention behind it will have better results. So, setting micro-intentions prior to anything you do is important. Especially before you sit down to connect with your Higher Self. Know why you are connecting, why you are eating, why you are going to work, etc. The why behind the what will guide you straight into your spiritual GPS system, your heart, and when you create and live from the heart, the electromagnetic force emitted will attract all things that you need to fulfill your intention. Therefore, it is vital to spend time each day connecting in silence to your Higher Self—using whatever tools helps you connect. For some, this can be nature; for All, it will include conscious breath.

A stands for Air.

"And God *breathed* into man, the *breath of life*, and man became a living being…" Breath is life. It was the first thing we did after birth and the last thing we'll do before leaving our bodies. It is our faithful companion and best friend throughout this incarnation. It is our constant reminder that we are grateful to be alive and that life is a gift. Breath is the purest form of free energy on planet Earth, and it is abundant, accessible, and a carries a high-vibration frequency, which ancient, wise sages of the past called "prana," "life force," "energy," "chi," and in Hebrew, as quoted in the Bible verse above, "Ruach" (Breath), which translates into "Spirit." If one is able to learn how to consciously work with this amazing Spirit Friend, there is nothing in the world that is impossible. First, you will overcome fear, anxiety, depression, ancestral karma, then even death. Once the physical body is cleansed through conscious breathing, the emotional/mental body will be integrated so that the energetic/spiritual body can shine its light, thus activating the bliss body, which is every person's birthright. I hope you're ready for this beautiful journey into the breath of life! In my years working as a psychiatrist, I have learned that breath is the most potent weapon and medicine against any physical, mental, or energetic illness. And, may I repeat, it is abundant, free, right under your nose, and waiting to heal as instructed with conscious awareness and direction.

We will start by exploring how the breath can cleanse the physical body. The body is a highly connected, intelligent, mathematical network of communicating cells, neurons, tissues, and organs that serves as a vessel of pure Divine intelligence. And that intelligence and information is found in the breath. Everything is energy, including our physical bodies. Our body at any time vibrates to the electromagnetic frequency of the emotions that our heart center is emitting. Thus, emotion = energy in motion. Trauma and unexpressed emotions are stored in our physical bodies as low-vibration emotions, such as guilt, shame or fear. For example, when we were younger, and our throat energy center wanted to express a melodic tone, but our mother shushed us, that energy was stored in the body as unexpressed emotion. Another example is with people who have been diagnosed with Post-Traumatic Stress Disorder. Navy Seals who witnessed the deaths of close beloved friends in combat and received a highly charged emotional shock to the system can store this experience as low-vibration emotions and can store the memories in the body as trauma. The higher the emotional charge, the greater the memory of the trauma. The physical body stores this trauma in the spine, muscles, fascia, the cellular memory, etc. The Navy Seal, after being trained in boot camp to suppress and repress rather than express the emotions associated with this trauma, stores the experience and associated emotions into the physical body. Thus, the trauma and low-vibration emotions associated with the trauma, which are stored in the body, are in constant communication with the mind, reminding it of the shock and emotions associated with the past trauma. Because the experiencer of the trauma never wants to re-experience the trauma again, they walk around in a state of constant sympathetic nervous system (fight/flight) activation, worried that the past trauma will happen again. At this point, the breath is following the mind. The breath will mirror the erratic, irrational, fearful rhythm of the thoughts of the mind. Thus, the past trauma not only invades the present moment but begins to determine the predictable future, as one is constantly worried that the past trauma will happen again in the future thus fulfilling its prophecy and further ingraining the trauma into the physical. Throughout this whole process, one will find that the breath has been unconsciously being breathed to the rhythm of the mostly subconscious irrational thoughts, which are unconsciously accepted as true. At any point, one can calm the mind by returning to a steady, calm, slow, rhythmic breathing pattern thus allowing the brain waves and mind to start following the conscious rhythm of the breath.

To clear the body of trauma on a physical level, the breath can serve as a powerful tool. In fact, daily, consistent breathwork is the

30

best medicine for PTSD. The breath/prana/chi is a high-vibration frequency. The law of entrainment states that as a high-vibration frequency permeates a lower vibration frequency, the lower vibration frequency or trauma will entrain to the higher vibration. Higher vibrations will entrain lower vibrations. This is why most married couples will entrain to the same frequency in order to live harmoniously together. Thus, the low vibration energies of guilt, shame, and fear associated with the trauma will often spontaneously release and flow out of the body during a conscious breathwork session. Thus, the physical body releases its stored traumas, lower-vibration emotions are entrained, and the physical body starts becoming cleansed into its original Divine blueprint of a body designed of pure energy, prana, life force, or the breath.

You see, the breath will either follow the mind, or the mind will follow the breath. The goal is to have the breath lead the way. You will never find anyone who is anxious while breathing "normally." You will never find anyone who is angry while breathing "normally." This is because the breath rate and rhythm are intimately connected to the rate and rhythm of the brain waves. When the breath is leading the way, we breathe at a rate of 4 to 6 breaths/minute compared to the average human who breathes 16 to 20 breaths/minute. Calm, slow, steady, quiet, and rhythmic inhales associate with a similar effortless release of the diaphragm, which signifies the beginning of the exhale. As you start to breathe at a consistent pattern and rate, this entrains the brain waves to start mirroring the respiratory cycle. The brain waves become calm, rhythmic, and slow and start entering brain wave states, such as alpha, where we can concentrate and focus on any creative project at hand or sink into the subtleties of the present moment. It is also in this state where we can start becoming aware of our thoughts, conditioning, and programming.

The Universe communicates with you through your brain waves. Thus, when the brain waves are calm and relaxed through the breath, the Universe can send you epiphanies and revelations through your crown chakra, as you are open, suggestible, and re-laxed. Think of it as when the breath is relaxed, the bandwidth of the mind increases and is open to epiphanic downloads from the Universe. When we are in beta brain waves, on the go, the sympa-thetic nervous system is activated (reactionary state of being); the Universe is not able to send you the messages you need in the moment because you are running on subconscious programming and conditioning based upon past memories and experiences. In fact, by the age of 35, 95% of all a human does is based on routine subconscious programming. When the breath, thus the brain waves, is relaxed to a slow, calm rhythm, theta brain waves start to occur frequently. In this brain wave state, we are open, suggestible, and calm and can start approaching, releasing, reprogramming, re-framing, or deleting old subconscious programming/trauma, condi-tioning, and outdated belief systems that no longer serve our emo-tional and mental health. If the breath/brain waves are not relaxed, most traumas cannot even be approached due to the fear surround-ing the past event. So, the key becomes at any given point to sur-render to the beauty of the present moment and watch the move-ment of Spirit (breath) within the body by returning one's attention to the breath. Thus, as we start to breathe at a rhythmic, relaxed rate, the mind will relax into the present moment, where the magic of the Universe is constantly happening. There is no anxiety (when the mind is worried about the future), depression (when the mind is regretting a past event), or trauma that can be present when we are flowing in a rhythmic, relaxed, continuous breath pattern.

Breath is sometimes referred to as the chord that ties the flesh to the soul. Imagine a silver chord entering through your crown chakra or top of your head. It first enters into your spiritual/energetic body, then the mental/emotional body, and then the physical body as it connects the soul to the mind to the body. All ancient cultures knew that the breath is Spirit. In Hebrew, the word is "Ruach," which means "Spirit." In the East, the word is "chi," which means "Spirit." In India, the word is "prana," which means "Spirit" or "life force." All great masters of the past have had an intimate relationship with Spirit or the breath. Written records indicate that before the master teacher Jesus ascended, he *breathed* on his disciples and said, "receive the Holy Spirit." It is also well documented that Jesus traveled through India and Nepal and was familiar with ancient breathing techniques, which he likely employed every day of his life but especially when he was hanging on the cross. The great master teacher Buddha sat under a tree and as he observed his breath, he found the enlightenment within himself as he merged with the breath and his Spirit and released the illusion of separation, or suffering. It is the unseen world that controls the seen world; however, most of us live our lives focusing on what is seen, thus giving our attention and control to the things that are external rather than internal. Thus, we start believing the illusions of the seen world, including the need for more and the illusion of separation. Then we start to believe that we lack, which is the cause of all suffering. Right now, there is a child in a third-world country, running around happy, without a care in the world. She has nothing to her name but does not suffer because she does not know or think that she lacks. As we start becoming aware of the breath in our daily practices, we start becoming aware and in alignment with the laws of the unseen world as revealed to us through the breath/Spirit—abundance, peace, harmony, neutrality, and love. In the Spirit world, there is no lack, thus there is no suffering. Therefore, it is good to adopt a practice of working with the breath.

Modern science is finally starting to catch up to the truths that our ancestors inherently knew. Yes, there are energetic freeways/pathways around our bodies sometimes referred to as meridians. Energy can travel along these meridians, and breath is key to cleansing these pathways. When conscious attention is given to the breath traveling along these pathways and is infused with a pure intention, the pathways are purified and cleansed, and energy can flow freely through our bodies. As we engage in daily, conscious breathwork, we will follow a course of cleansing and energizing our physical body, calming and reprogramming our mental/emotional body, and then awakening into our energetic/bliss body once the conditioning is cleared. Bliss is our birthright and it is not a matter of addition to obtain it but subtracting all the programmed beliefs and conditioning to reveal the bliss underneath it all. The breath will cleanse the physical body, quiet the mind, and open an eternal well-spring of beauty and life that springs forth from the heart. Quiet the mind through the breath, and the heart will speak. Within it, you will find a Divine blueprint, a renewed purpose, and the entire Universe.

R stands for Rest/Sleep.

Sleep and rest are vital to the physical body, mind, and Spirit. Physically, this is when our bodies enter in a rhythmic breath, slow brain-wave state, and our vitality, life force, neurotransmitters, proteins and hormones, are replenished. Mentally/emotionally, this is when our body is able to clear out the garbage the mind has accumulated throughout the day. When one cannot sleep, such as in bipolar disorder, there is an excess amount of energy and thoughts, which have not been cleaned out by sleep. This leads to racing thoughts, emotions, and erratic behavior. It is essential that you get sufficient rest. There are many different opinions about what happens energetically when the body falls asleep. Some believe that the soul or spirit is able to once again return to Source and freely roam in the astral or cosmic consciousness realm. Some believe when we sleep and dream, it has no meaning at all and that it is simply karmic patterns playing themselves out. This may be true 98% of the time, but there are also those times where one receives a clear, poignant message through a dream. Spiritual masters have learned how to master the dream world so that they are able to intentionally create energy in their dreams that carries on into their daily, three-dimensional lives. Either way, sleep is vital for restoration of energy on a physical, emotional, and spiritual level. Most bodies need seven to nine hours of sleep. For insomnia, the best medicine is to practice rhythmic breathing. Yoga nidra, also known as yogic sleep, is a set of beautiful ancient practices that will help you fall asleep while also reprogramming your subconscious mind during sleep. I recommend that you download Insight Timer on your cellular phone and search for "yoga nidra for sleep" whenever you are suffering from insomnia.

T stands for Temperance, Discipline, or Self-Control.

Temperance is what prevents control by external circumstances or desires. It is what allows the Higher Self to exercise its capacity to choose what is best and needed rather than what is wanted. The physical body can become addicted to the chemistry of suffering and will often start craving external desires, which may promote temporary relief but never permanent satisfaction. Self-control will allow one to resist external desires and act in a way that promotes permanent peace and happiness. This includes having the discipline to wake up each morning to watch the sunrise, drinking water upon awakening, choosing to eat a whole-food diet, choosing to be consistent with morning meditations, etc. There is no love without sacrifice, self-control, or temperance. Or, as some would say, there is no shakti without bhakti. Learn to listen to the internal guidance and wisdom rather than the addicted physical body or scattered and contradictory mental body.

To summarize, love is the most powerful medicine on the planet. It is the power that connects, heals, and integrates. For any mental health problem, first seek to find a loving, like-minded, accepting, supportive community. Then start by optimizing the key factors described in the acronym, NEWSTART. This will be the foundation for health as we move into each specific mental health condition.

On a side note, if you want to know if you have a good doctor, ask yourself if you have a changed attitude when you leave the office. The best doctors will leave you with a changed attitude regarding your health. Why is this important? The brain has its own natural pharmacy and is able to produce all the healing chemicals it needs. When one is able to change their attitude, their brain will naturally start producing the right chemicals it needs to heal or integrate itself back into wholeness. So, next time you are doctor shopping, please remember to find someone who has a positive attitude and is able to connect with you on a level that encourages you to view your health condition from a perspective of renewed hope, faith, and love.

B. Staple Supplements

From my experience, the following three supplements can be helpful for most people. The benefits of taking them regularly far outweigh any potential side effects. The three "universal supplements" that I would recommend are magnesium, fish oil, and CBD oil. Please, however, do your own research. Please also understand that supplement indicates that it is only necessary when you are not getting the proper nutrition from your regular diet. First and foremost, eating a healthy, balanced diet is the best "supplement."

I will, however, state that I truly believe CBD oil can be beneficial for most human beings. It is helpful for almost every psychiatric condition as well as helpful for getting people off of psychiatric medications. Science has just started to uncover the potential that lies within this sacred plant we call marijuana. I know from clinical practice and from trusted peers that consistent use of CBD oil helps the entire physical, mental, and emotional body. It helps with pain, anxiety, depression, psychosis, and trauma and helps in the process of safely getting off of medications. Not to mention the potential it is showing for help with cancer treatment. CBD decreases neuroinflammation, which is the root cause of many diseases. Thus, it helps treat most diseases. However, once again, please do your own research. A simple google search of "CBD benefits" will lead to a wealth of information.

RECEPT is a trusted brand of hemp oil that is effectively absorbed, third-party tested, from a trusted source, and can provide quick absorption and effect. Most people feel the effects within 5 to 10 minutes. This product is available on primemybody.com.

CHAPTER 4:
DEPRESSION

Depression is an opportunity for spiritual evolution and a transition state in consciousness.

A. A Conscious Paradigm of Depression

The "dark night of the soul," also known as depression, is a natural process of an expanding spiritual life. In order to experience the resurrection, one must experience the crucifixion. Energetically speaking, the dark night of the soul is a series of episodes of "dark" crises, which leads to the ultimate birth process. There is no birth without a birth process. During the episodes of crisis, one will learn how to let go of all that does not serve, surrender to the Universal force of love, and emerge a more conscious, aware, joyful being. The ultimate end goal of the whole process is to emerge a joyful being that realizes that Source/God is in All and that joyful, humble service to the All is the highest dharma of existence.

Depression from a Western perspective is a disease that is indicated by the presence of five out of a possible nine symptoms—which were made up by psychiatrists who formulated these conditions based on often biased and hand-selected research articles. It is often the people who control the money that influence which studies are discarded (the ones not in alignment with the promotion of their medications) and which ones are included in standard publications (often times, the studies that are in alignment with their views and that promote their medications). When one goes to a psychiatrist and fits the checklist of symptoms, he or she will be labeled as having major depressive disorder and will be started on psychiatric medications that will alter serotonin levels in the body, often temporarily numbing the depressive symptoms while never actually dealing with the root cause of the symptoms. Once the body naturally adjusts to the chemical imbalance that the medication is causing, the depressive symptoms can once again return because the cause has never been addressed. Sometimes psychiatric medications may effectively numb the symptoms while one is in a state of crisis, allowing the person to effectively avoid suicide and continue to function in a sick society. The problem is that the root cause of the symptoms is never addressed; the patient just detaches from his or her situation. Usually the actual problem isn't that the patient is sick but that he or she is trying to adjust and function in a sick society. So instead of trying to fit into a sick society, perhaps these patients would benefit from trying to find a community that accepts them as they are without trying to change them.

From an energetic standpoint, depressive symptoms occur when one continuously experiences low-frequency emotions, such as guilt, shame, or fear. These symptoms can be traced back to thoughts such as, *What's wrong with me? I'm not good enough... I shouldn't have...*, etc. These thoughts can be traced back to conditioned belief patterns, which have been subconsciously ingrained in one's psyche since childhood. These belief patterns can be traced back to how one received love as child. If a person received love from his father by being perfect in all he does, then he will continue to believe that he has to be perfect in his adult life. For instance, if a child received love from her mother by going to church, she will learn that one way to receive love from her mother is to continue to go to church. This changes as one reaches puberty and teenage years, as peer influence has a major effect on the child's belief system. Many children receive love in junior high for doing well in school, keeping up with the latest trends, excelling at athletics, being admired by the opposite sex, etc. These are all ways which one learns is a way to receive love, which the child so desperately needs in order to grow. These children will continue to live out these patterns until these patterns no longer serve them and they are forced to examine the root of the belief systems and reframe, delete, or restructure them to be in alignment with the beliefs that promote their wellbeing and joy.

Depression also occurs when one continues to exhaust their mind by having continuous, repetitive, thought cycles that do not lead to liberation but to confusion and low-vibration emotions. If you were to stop and actually write down all thoughts in a day, you would find that most of your thoughts are untrue, often contradict each other, and try to control external circumstances that are impossible to control. It's like having a roommate in your mind that lies, contradicts himself, and tries to do impossible things all day. During depression, one is spending all day listening to the mind, or roommate, and believing all of the thoughts as if they were true. This leads to low-vibration emotions, which permeate into the body, mind, and spirit, therefore causing insomnia, variable appetite, isolation, anhedonia, guilt, difficulty concentrating, agitation, hopelessness, and eventually suicidal thoughts.

From a spiritual standpoint, depression is a transition state in consciousness. It is a protective mechanism of the body signaling you to slow down, rest, and adjust your lifestyle to one that is conducive to your happiness. Keep in mind, depression is not the same thing as grief. Grief is a natural process of feeling sad for the loss of something or someone you truly loved and is a necessary part of human life. It is necessary to grieve and not suppress your sadness when faced with loss. It is a beautiful part of the human process. Rushed psychiatrists often mislabel grief as major depression, and these "patients" are often started on antidepressants, which actually interfere with the grieving process and numb down emotions that need to be expressed in order to fully process the grief. This leads to unresolved grief, and the grief can then resurface because it has not been processed and integrated.

Depression is a sign of spiritual evolution and can be looked at as a transition state of consciousness. It is an opportunity to become aware of the things, systems, beliefs, and people who no longer serve you and detach from the familiar into the void some call darkness. In this darkness, one can see the wound (cause of sadness) through which the healing light can enter. And if one chooses, he can allow this light of awareness to enter through the wound and purge the old programs that no longer serve him and emerge as a higher frequency being. The greatest battle you will ever face is with the darkness within your own soul. This means that perception is creation. What you perceive in the world is a reflection of the conditioned mind. It is the mind that processes everything and interprets it as darkness. However, when you face this darkness in your own mind and are able to reframe it into light, you will be able to see through the delusions of separation and darkness and find the light within the previously supposed darkness. You will even be able to find the light within depression and be able to see how it is an opportunity for growth and a step in the evolution of your consciousness. After overcoming all of this, you will have the keys to the consciousness to help others who find themselves in a similar experience as the one you overcame. And through the darkness we become aware of the beautiful, divine, cosmic play we are gifted to experience. And we realize we have but two choices, love or fear. Depression is an opportunity to look into the areas of your life where you have been choosing fear and to choose love and connection instead. And if you find yourself in the darkness consciously, you can rejoice for you now know that joy comes in the morning and he who is "forgiven" much can love much. The greater the darkness or depression one has experienced; the greater one can appreciate the light of the morning. The greatest souls to have ever walked this earth have experienced the dark night of the soul and used it as an experience to grow in love and elevate their consciousness.

During your transformation, you might feel like everything is falling apart, but in reality, everything is coming together for your highest good. You're being pushed to evolve and get out of your comfort zone so you can live and experience your true greatness. Embrace and welcome change. The unknown void referred to as darkness is the only place you can create from. Depression breaks you out of your comfort zone of subconscious programming and forces you to take an honest look at all areas of your life and make changes that are in accordance with your true purpose and happiness.

Depression from a Western perspective is often viewed as a dis-ease or a symptom of weakness or failure. This viewpoint was adopted by the general Western collective consciousness by creating a book called the *Diagnostic and Statistical Manual of Mental Disorders* and loads of effective advertising. This advertising has misled the general public to believe that depression is secondary to a chemical imbalance in the brain. This is a flat-out lie. First of all, there is no way to measure the chemicals in the brain effectively, and no psychiatrist ever does this prior to diagnosing or prescribing potentially addictive and harmful medications, which actually create a chemical imbalance rather than fixing one. The *DSM-5* has labeled anybody who experiences five out of nine symptoms of depression for two weeks or longer as having major depressive disorder and recommends placing the patient on medication, most commonly serotonin reuptake inhibitors (SSRIs). When someone who is "depressed" goes to see a psychiatrist and is labeled with depression by this "authority" figure, they often start to believe that they have a disease and there is something wrong with them. This thought alone starts to resonate through the body, and the body starts to code for proteins, hormones, and chemical messengers that are in alignment with the idea that *there is something wrong with me.* As soon as someone believes that they have a chemical imbalance, it actually causes one. Then, the person who is depressed starts feeling like they are abnormal, which leads to isolation, which leads to even further depression. Then they are started on standard Western medications. These medications can be fairly successful at numbing down the symptoms one is experiencing. However, over the course of time, these medications actually end up causing a chemical imbalance, making it nearly impossible to actually address the cause of the depression, which often originates at an energetic or spiritual level and is presenting itself as a symptom so that the lesson can be learned and the changes made in order to evolve into a higher energetic vibration. All Western anti-depressant medications will typically shut down or numb energy centers in the body, making them ineffective. Most antidepressant medications can effectively numb the frontal lobe and sufficiently chemically lobotomize the patient so that they can continue to func-tion in their dysfunction. Most Western antidepressants will cause sexual dysfunction and shut down the second chakra or center of creative energy (occurs more than 70% of the time). When the frontal lobe is numbed, it makes it nearly impossible to exercise the judgment needed to actually start addressing the root cause of the depression because a sense of judgment and intuition is numbed. After several months, the body becomes used to being numb and becomes addicted to the feeling of numbness or chemical imbal-ance that is now being perceived as normal.

This whole time, the actual cause of the depression is not being dealt with. For example, if the cause of depression was being in an abusive relationship, or continuing to go to a job that is not in align-ment with one's purpose, the person will continue to cause daily harm to themselves by continuing in the cause of the symptoms while numbing themselves down enough to continue to function in their dysfunctional situation. Because the body and mind are numbed, they will not be able to hear or respond to the subtle promptings of the heart and intuition. Therefore, although the per-son will be able to function "normally" in society, the actual cause of the problem is not being dealt with and will continue to cause stress and disease on a subtle level. It seems as if Western psychi-atric medications are very effective at numbing down low-frequency emotional vibrations, such as guilt, shame, or fear, temporarily. This can serve helpful for the population that just wants to be "normal" and "fit in" to today's modern society. The truth is, however, that each human being is a unique individual "note" in the great cosmic symphony of the Creator and is meant to stand out and not fit in. The depressive symptoms were likely trying to awaken the experi-encer that it was time to detach from something or someone caus-ing low-vibration emotions and transition to a higher state of con-sciousness.

So, to reiterate, Western psychiatric medications do not deal with the cause of the depressive symptoms and thus the symptoms, though temporarily numbed, can reappear at any time. For example, imagine a negative of a photograph. The negative symbolizes the actual cause or source of the depression. The photograph symbolizes the symptoms of depression. Western medications try to numb or destroy the photograph (symptoms) while never actually dealing with the cause (the negative). Therefore, even if you destroy the photograph, the photograph or symptoms can always reappear because the negative or actual cause has not been addressed. Eventually, the antidepressant medications will cause a chemical imbalance, create a physical and mental addiction, and stop working. At this point, the Western psychiatric practice is to increase the dose, or add another antidepressant, or even sometimes add low-dose antipsychotics or other medications that still do not address the root cause but only cause more side effects. This cycle continues until most patients are addicted to many different psychiatric medications, numb to their own feelings and energetic guidance, and end up hopeless and even suicidal.

Your attitude towards depression will determine how it is processed and dealt with. At this point, it is important to understand that from a spiritual or energetic perspective, depression can be viewed as a stage in our conscious evolution individually and collectively. It serves as a GPS system to guide the person to his or her own true happiness. In order to experience bliss and happiness, one must have first experienced the opposite polarity, such as sadness or grief. The greatest souls on the planet have experienced depression and used it as a stepping-stone to a higher level of consciousness.

B. My Testimony of Depressive Experiences

I have personally experienced "major depression" multiple times in my life. My first experience was when I had no concept of what depression was and thus experienced it rather unconsciously. My brothers had left for college, and my parents moved to a new city where I didn't know anybody. I was separated from my friends and community and found myself isolated in my room, not eating, losing weight, being unable to sleep, not wanting to do anything, and wondering if there was any meaning to life. At this point in my life, I was in high school and unconscious to what was going on. I slept through most of it and eventually found a community at church. The symptoms gradually disappeared as I found purpose and meaning by falling in love with Jesus and becoming active in my church community.

The second time I experienced major depression was when my psychiatry residency program shut down after my third year of residency. I had one year left to complete residency, and I moved locations for my final year. At this time, I had wandered far away from my spirituality and was stuck in the belief that I had to go back to church, read the Bible, and pray to Jesus in order to find peace. These beliefs had been ingrained in me since childhood. After becoming dissatisfied with the hypocrisy and lack of passion in the church, I prayed to God to wait for me, telling Him I would be back after I had explored the "world" and all it had to offer. After seven years of "running away from God" by partying and partaking in all the pleasures the world had to offer, I was stuck in guilt, shame, and fear, believing that I was a "sinner" and needed to repent and go back to God. I was also in a relationship with a beautiful girl; she was like a best friend, but deep down I knew she was not meant to be my wife. I stayed in the relationship because I thought that was what I was supposed to do. This also caused a tremendous amount of guilt and shame. I continued in the relationship and decided to move out of Los Angeles to Seattle, where I would propose to my girlfriend, go back to church, and go back to being the good Christian man I was raised to be. This was the best plan I could think of at the time—flee the city of temptations and go back to being a good church boy.

This plan totally backfired. After moving to Seattle, I found myself even more full of guilt, shame, and fear. While attempting to finish my last year of residency, I found myself paralyzed with paranoia. I thought I was such a bad person for having strayed from church and God. I continuously beat myself up in my mind and believed the negative thoughts I was having, which led to constant guilt, shame, and fear. When one experiences these low-vibration emotions in severe depression, certain energies or entities that are attracted to these low energies can start manifesting. The thought that I was sinful would lead to avoiding eye contact, which would lead to thoughts that people were watching me, which would lead to hiding, etc. My subconscious beliefs patterns that I was ingrained with as a child as well as my parents constantly criticizing me led me to believe I was a bad person. This was during my last year of residency of medical school. Each morning I would wake up paralyzed by fear of the day ahead and unable to get out of bed. I attempted to pray and read my Bible for one to two hours each morning before going to work, but this would make me feel even guiltier. During the day, I would walk around not wanting to be in my own body or to even be alive. The low-vibration emotions pervaded my body, and every step I took was arduous. Each meeting I sat through was like hell. I could not make eye contact with anybody in fear that they would see me. This lasted for three to five months, and I would never wish this experience upon anybody.

By the grace of God and consistent support from my fiancée at the time, I was somehow able to muster up the courage to go to work and complete residency. I cried like a baby when I received my residency certificate, not because I was proud of myself but because of the hell I had been through to obtain a piece of paper. I called in sick many times. I contemplated suicide many times, believing the world would be a better place without me. I tried to go back to church, but at this point in my life, I no longer "fit in." The people who used to love and praise me at church now didn't want anything to do with me. This whole time I was lying to my parents about living with my girlfriend, as I knew they would freak out. I was trying to please them by going to church and couldn't tell them the truth of who I was because I knew they would not approve and would continue to push church, the Bible, and their beliefs on me. At this time, I started seeing a therapist and taking Lexapro, an

SSRI, which numbed me long enough for me to finish residency. Western treatment at this time was a blessing, as it can be in times of extreme life or death situations. It helped me survive and complete residency. It was easy to be numbed, as actual intuition is not really needed during psychiatry residency.

This severe episode of depression eventually forced me to take an honest look at my life. It forced me to reexamine what I truly believed. It helped me see religion in a different light. It helped me start unplugging from the belief systems that no longer served me. It forced me to take an honest look at my parents and to start healing my animosity towards them. It made me take an honest look at my relationship with my ex-fiancée and be truthful about how I truly felt. It was the most difficult time in my life but also the most pivotal point in my life that led me to start exploring who I truly was and what I truly wanted rather than what my parents wanted for me. After not listening to my spiritual guidance system (the intelligence of the heart) for so long, I had learned to effectively ignore my heart. Each day it would subtly tell me that the relationship I was in was not for marriage, but I refused to listen and ignored the subtle promptings. Each day my heart would tell me that the lifestyle I was living was not serving my happiness, but I ignored it. Finally, the Universe had to kick me in the ass and force me to take an honest look at myself, and I am thankful for it to this day.

The third experience with major depression was a totally different experience, as I went through it consciously. I knew I was experiencing depressive symptoms. I knew that it was a transition state in consciousness. I knew that it was causing me to pause and examine my life and unplug and change the circumstances that were no longer serving me. I knew that it was causing me to listen to my intuition and heart and start following that rather than the analytical, rational mind. At the time I was blessed with a teacher and mentor who could guide me, tune me, and point me to the right tools at the right moment. This episode of "depression" was preparing me to leave a job that, though I loved, was no longer in alignment with my true heart's purpose. It was a springboard to detach from media and people who were no longer in alignment with the direction my heart was yearning for. It created space for me to start filling my life with things and people that did serve that and me were in alignment with my purpose. It led me to a deeper connection with breath and sacred music, which would become my passion in life.

I have also been through several other minor depressive episodes, and each time, looking back, they have all been transitions states in consciousness to help me process, release, and take the next step forward in life. Depression is the Universe trying to work for you, not against you. It is the Universe trying to help guide you into your North Star of purpose by causing you to detach in the unknown state some call darkness. This unknown place, detached from what is familiar, is the only place you can create a new life from.

Depression is not a disease you should feel bad about. It is not a chemical imbalance in your brain. There is nothing fundamentally wrong with you for experiencing depressive symptoms. You do not need pity from people when experiencing depression. Depression is a transition state of consciousness. It is an opportunity to detach from what doesn't make you happy and attach to what does. It is an opportunity to evolve in consciousness so that you can eventually help people. It is the ultimate paradox in life where one experiences sadness in order to truly appreciate happiness. Depression is a blessing in disguise. It is an opportunity to take a look at your belief systems and reframe them to what is in alignment with your purpose and path. Depression is a sign of spiritual evolution. To anyone experiencing depression, please do not get down on yourself or beat yourself up. Instead, know that the Universe is working for you and not against you. Know that there is nothing fundamentally wrong with you. Know that you are not alone. Know that you do not need to isolate. But most of all, hold on and don't give up, for joy comes in the morning.

C. How Western Psychiatry Treats Depression

Unfortunately, most Western psychiatrists are abiding in a system that has trained them to ask about a checklist of symptoms then prescribe medications. There is no time to closely look at or address the root cause of the symptoms. If you go see a traditional Western psychiatrist for depressive symptoms, no matter what the cause is, the most likely cycle will be: being placed on medications, the medications stop working, the psychiatrist increasing the dose of medications and/or trying or adding a different medication. When the symptoms become severe and suicidal thoughts emerge, this could mean a trip to the local inpatient psychiatric hospital, where you will be locked up and likely forced to take medications until your spirit is broken down enough to simply give up and comply to the system. If you resist taking psychiatric medications while in the inpatient psychiatric hospital, your stay most likely will be prolonged.

When you have trialed multiple antidepressants, failed at least three different medications, and still are severely depressed, this can lead to a referral for electroconvulsive therapy, where you will be hooked up to electrodes, which cause seizures in your brain. Nobody really knows how it works. The theory is that it shakes up the brain enough so that it is "re-wired" so that you either forget you were depressed or no longer feel depressed. Modern published literature will tell you it is "mostly" safe, with only slight chance of memory loss. However, many patients who have experienced ECT will tell you otherwise. According to some statistics, for major severe refractory depression, ECT can temporarily relieve the symptoms up to 70% of the time. However, from my clinical experience, the depressive symptoms will most often return. My hypothesis is, once again, that this is because the root cause of the depression is not being dealt with.

If you are going to proceed with electroconvulsive therapy, please do so with caution and at your own risk. It is not well understood, and there have been some patients who never recover after having ECT.

Another treatment on the rise for severe refractory depression is transcranial magnetic stimulation. Once again, nobody really knows how this treatment works. The provider will use a magnet to stimulate certain parts of the brain, and after a certain number of treatments, the patient seems to improve. Although this treatment option may be less barbaric then ECT, once again, the root cause of the depression is not being dealt with and the symptoms are likely to return. Also, the treatment is a relatively new, and time will tell what the long-term side effects may be. Please do careful research prior to opting to go forward with this treatment.

D. Tapering off of Psychiatric Medications

If you desire to safely taper off of psychiatric medications, I highly recommend you find a physician who is attuned to natural treatments and cooperate with your physician to find a gradual taper plan while utilizing natural healing modalities. If you go "cold turkey" or stop your psychiatric medications too quickly, you may experience withdrawal symptoms, such as dizziness, loss of coordination, fatigue, tingling, burning, blurred vision, insomnia, and vivid dreams, often referred to as "brain zaps." Occasionally, you may also experience nausea, diarrhea, flu-like symptoms, irritability, anxiety, and crying spells. When helping a patient wean off of SSRIs, 5-HTP or Saint John's Wort can be safely utilized. I recommend working with your physician to safely taper off of medications and to avoid the possibility of serotonin syndrome (although I've never witnessed this in my practice), which can produce sudden onset symptoms of fever, shivering, sweating, diarrhea, confusion, and muscle spasms. I have never witnessed anybody experience serotonin syndrome while utilizing 5-HTP or Saint John's Wort while reducing the SSRI dosage. 5-HTP 50mg or Saint John's Wort 900mg may be used while you work with your physician. A usual taper can be done by decreasing the drug to half the daily dosage every two to four weeks, depending on how your body reacts and how long you've been on the medication.

Trusted colleagues have also been successfully utilizing CBD oil as part of the tapering process and found that tapers are more successful with less side effects when CBD oil is part of the taper regimen.

E. Natural Alternative Treatments for Depression

The best treatment for depression is an authentic community where you can find loving connection. You can find such communities these days through meetup.com, at a local yoga studio, church, or by joining a group related to one of your hobbies. Most depressed people, however, do not have the energy or sociability to join a group, so the following are alternative treatments.

Please remember that NEWSTART™ is the best medicine, even for depression. Specifically, spending at least 30 minutes three times a week engaged in exercise that involves any sort of rhythmic breathing, such as swimming, jogging, yoga, etc., is essential. It is also recommended you spend at least 30 minutes a day in nature doing relaxation techniques, such as meditation or rhythmic breathing.

Nutritional Psychiatry: Treatments for Depression

What you eat directly affects the structure and function of your brain as well as your mood. Vitamins, minerals, and antioxidants can help protect and nourish the brain from oxidative stress. Oxidative stress produces free radicals, which damage your cells. Serotonin is a key neurotransmitter that helps regulate mood, sleep, and appetite. It is now known that 95% of serotonin is produced in the gut lining, not the brain! The gut lining is a reservoir of neurons, as well as "good" bacteria, which protect your gut lining, help absorb nutrients, and help the communication pathways between your gut and brain. Food directly affects your mood as well as your brain function. The gut can be called the "second brain."

Please pay attention to how different foods make you feel. Each body is different. A good place to start is by cutting out sugar and all processed foods that cause inflammation. In addition, try to add fermented foods like sauerkraut, pickles, kimchi, and kombucha. Some people will do better on a dairy-free diet. Avoiding grains can also help protect your gut from inflammation and "leaky gut syndrome." Try a clean diet for two to three weeks and see how you feel. Each body is different, and it is important to find a clean diet that is maintainable and helps you feel at your best.

Foods to Avoid

Alcohol – Alcohol is frequently associated with depression. It is unclear whether it is a direct toxic effect or if the effect is indirect, as alcohol causes nutritional deficiencies. Depression is usually the most severe three to four weeks after a person stops drinking. It is recommended the person restrict alcohol intake and correct nutritional deficiencies by taking magnesium and B vitamins.

Aspartame – Many studies are correlating depression to the intake of aspartame. A hypothesized mechanism of actions is that aspartame inhibits glucose-stimulated uptake of tryptophan into the brain. It is advised that depressed patients avoid aspartame for 2-3 weeks. If they feel no difference, they can reintroduce aspartame to see if it causes a shift in their mood.

Caffeine – According to one observational study, patients who consumed large amounts of caffeine (750mg/day or more) had significantly higher scores on depression rating scales. The mechanism of action is unclear; however, decreasing caffeine intakes slowly and gradually may help improve long-term mood.

Monosodium Glutamate – Case reports correlate the consumption of MSG to recurrent bouts of depression. It is advised that depressed patients avoid the intake of MSG.

*Reactive Hypoglycemia – Depression can be correlated to decreased blood sugar levels. This is often seen in elderly hospitalized patients with nutritional deficits, who lack amino acids to make neurotransmitters. The depressed mood often exacerbates in late morning or late afternoon (before mealtimes). Usually, at this point these, patients crave sweets for transient relief, then another exacerbation. It is best for these patients to go on a dietary program to stabilize blood sugar levels. This could include avoiding refined sugar, caffeine, and alcohol; consumption of small, frequent meals; and supplementation with micronutrients such as chromium, magnesium and B vitamins. This may be an effective way of stabilizing the blood glucose levels and stabilizing mood fluctuations throughout the day.

*Candidiasis – It is hypothesized that candidiasis can cause depression. Some practitioners report that an "anti-Candida" program, which consists of oral nystatin and avoiding refined sugar, yeast-containing foods, and total carbohydrates, can relieve depressive symptoms, especially for women who have had recurrent vaginal yeast infections. It may be helpful to try an anti-Candida program, especially for women who have been treated with antibiotics, oral contraceptives, or systemic glucocorticoids.

Nutritional Supplements

L-Tryptophan – works by increasing serotonin levels and is most effective for those with serotonin deficiency who have responded positively to SSRIs in the past. Evidence suggests it can be helpful for those with mild to moderate depressive symptoms.

Please note that if you are already on an SSRI, L-tryptophan may help increase the efficacy of the medicine; however, it may also increase the chances of toxicity (serotonin syndrome), which can be deadly. I have never witnessed this in my seven years of psychiatric practice; however, this must be stated for safety reasons.

When starting SSRI treatment, it may be beneficial to co-administer up to 2g/day of L-tryptophan for up to four weeks to enhance the antidepressant effect. This modality seems to be safe and beneficial. Supplementation with niacinamide seems to increase the efficacy of L-tryptophan by inhibiting the enzyme tryptophan pyrrolase, which breaks down tryptophan in the liver.

For mild to moderate depressive symptoms: L-Tryptophan 2-3g/day combined with 1-2g/day of niacinamide, in two divided doses per day (between meals or at bedtime) can be effective.

Note: Do not take L-Tryptophan with 5-HTP; select one or the other.

L-5-Hydroxytrptophan (5-HTP) – is an immediate precursor of serotonin. Some studies show that 5-HTP is just as effective as or is more effective than SSRIs and is better tolerated, with less side effects. It is a good treatment option for mild to moderate depressive symptoms and works by providing serotonergic support.

Again, choose either L-Tryptophan or 5-HTP for depressive symptoms and not both. L-Tryptophan is synthesized to not only serotonin but also niacin and picolinic acid and a provides broader spectrum of benefits; however, some practitioners seem to believe that 5-HTP may be more effective in their clinical practice.

For mild to moderate depressive symptoms, take 5-HTP 50-200mg two to three times a day.

It is not advised that 5-HTP be combined with SSRIs for the possible risk of serotonin syndrome.

L-Tyrosine – Western science hypothesizes that low epinephrine levels may be linked to depressive symptoms. L-Tyrosine is a precursor to norepinephrine. More studies are necessary to determine optimal dosage of L-Tyrosine. It is possible that those who respond well to mood elevation after administration of amphetamine or SNRIs may respond better to L-Tyrosine.

For mild to moderate depressive symptoms with low energy take L-tyrosine 500mg twice a day. This is best if taken on empty stomach with carbohydrates.

Omega-3 fatty acids – Many double-blind studies indicate that supplementation with fish oil or with fatty acids present in fish oil, such as eicosatetraenoic acid (EPA) and docosahexaenoic acid (DHA), produced significant benefits for those with mild to moderate depression. DHA by itself does not seem to improve depressive symptoms; therefore, the ratio of DHA to EPA is important to consider. It is believed that EPA may have a beneficial effect on cell membranes and improve signal transduction, which may improve depressive symptoms. More studies need to be done to find the optimal dosage of omega-3 fatty acids for depression. The most effective preparations have at least a 60% EPA to DHA ratio.

For mild to moderate depressive symptoms in patients who have low fish intake, take1-2g/day of omega-3 fatty acid with at least 60% EPA to DHA ratio (pg. 1050 cutoff).

Folic acid – In select cases, depression can result from folate deficiency. Folic acid supplementation has been shown to be helpful for women with new onset depression when combined with Prozac.

For women with new onset depression who are taking an SSRI, folic acid 500 micrograms/day may reduce side effects and aid efficacy of the SSRI.

Vitamin B6 – Vitamin B6 plays a role in serotonin synthesis. Women who use oral contraceptives may be more susceptible to Vitamin B6 deficiency, which can lead to depressive symptoms.

For women who are on oral contraceptives with mild to moderate depressive symptoms, Vitamin B6 20-50mg/day may be helpful.

Magnesium – Plasma, serum, and white blood cell magnesium levels have been found to be significantly lower in patients with depression, leading researchers to believe magnesium deficiency plays a role in depressive symptoms.

Patients who have a low-magnesium diet (mostly fast food) may improve with magnesium.

Take magnesium L-threonate 200-300mg three to four times/day. iMagT from Sabre Sciences is a trusted brand with good absorption and effect.

Iron is a key component of norepinephrine and serotonin synthesis. For menstruating women, vegetarians, and people taking regular nonsteroidal anti-inflammatory drugs, iron may be a helpful supplement to improve mood and concentration. Have your iron levels tested by your primary care physician and take iron supplements as directed.

S-Adenosylmethionine (SAMe) – Has been proven to be an effective treatment for depression in several double-blind studies. Generally, S-Adenosylmethionine works more quickly than SSRIs and is well tolerated. Side effects can include headaches, anxiety, and mild gastrointestinal disturbances. S-Adenosylmethionine can sometimes flip a depressed bipolar patient from depressed to hypomania, so use with caution.

For the patient seeking an alternative to SSRIs that may have a quicker onset of action and less side effects, take SAMe 200-400mg two to three times a day.

Acetyl-L-Carnitine (ALC) – Has shown some promise in Alzheimer's disease as well as worked better for depressive symptoms in elderly depressed patients than conventional treatments.

For elderly depressed patients, take ALC 1.5-2.0g/day

Vitamin B12 – Some clinicians and patients report significant improvement in mood and energy from vitamin B12.

For those with low energy and depressive symptoms, it may be useful to take vitamin B12 (hydroxocobalamin) 1,000mg intramuscularly as needed (usually every one to two weeks).

Myers' cocktail – The modified "Myers' cocktail," which consists of magnesium, calcium, B vitamins, and vitamin C, has been found to be effective against acute asthma attacks, migraines, fatigue (including chronic fatigue syndrome), fibromyalgia, acute muscle spasm, upper respiratory tract infections, chronic sinusitis, seasonal allergic rhinitis, cardiovascular disease, and other disorders.

For those patients with low energy and fatigue and depressive symptoms, IV injections of Myers' Cocktail may be helpful.

Multivitamin – Some studies have shown that supplementation with a multivitamin for a year may improve mood. The theory is that the many micronutrients found in the vitamin may have a positive effect.

Hormones

Thyroid Hormone – may be the most underutilized treatment for depression. Even in some patients who test normal thyroid levels, thyroid hormone may be a useful augmentation or even treatment for depression. Dr. Alan Gaby writes in his book *Nutritional Medicine* that up to 40-50% of patients treated for chronic depression responded to thyroid hormone and about 85% of those patients who benefited had normal laboratory tests for thyroid function. Dr. Gaby prefers using desiccated thyroid to levothyroxine, as he has found it more effective in clinical practice. (Gaby, 2011).

For augmentation of SSRIs or traditional antidepressant medication, Triodothyronine 5.0-37.5 micrograms/day or levothyroxine 100-300 micrograms/day can help with clinical improvement of depressive symptoms.

Triiodothyronine appeared to be more effective than equivalent doses of levothyroxine.

Thyroid hormone is sometimes used as a primary treatment of depressive symptoms and can be helpful, but it is important to find a physician who is comfortable with this treatment and also have your thyroid hormones tested prior to treatment. Please note that even if your thyroid levels seem are normal on laboratory tests, but you are experiencing symptoms of hypothyroidism, thyroid treatment can be helpful.

Melatonin – One study found that 3mg/day of melatonin at bedtime helped improve symptoms of morning depression vs. placebo in perimenopausal and postmenopausal women. For menopause-related depression, it may be beneficial to take melatonin 3mg at bedtime

Dehydroepiandrosterone (DHEA) – Especially in chronically stressed patients who have adrenal insufficiency, DHEA can help ameliorate symptoms of depression.

For men, take 10-20 micrograms/day; for women, take 5-15 micrograms/day.

Herbs/Plant Medicine

St. John's Wort (*Hypericum perforatum*) – Many double-blind studies have demonstrated that St. John's Wort is just as effective as, or more effective than, Prozac, Zoloft, and several other antidepressant medications, with less side effects.

St. John's Wort may be the best alternative to medications in people under the age of 50.

For mild to moderate depression, 900mg/day in three divided doses may be helpful.

In cases of severe depression, one may combine St. John's Wort with 5-HTP 50-100mg three times per day.

Although side effects are rare, they can consist of gastrointestinal symptoms, allergic reactions, fatigue, and restlessness. It does not cause sedation and does not interact with alcohol. It should not be combined with SSRIs or trazodone for the minimal risk of serotonin syndrome. Also, one should note that St. John's Wort induces cytochrome P450 in the liver, which means medications such as warfarin, digoxin, oral contraceptives, anticonvulsants, calcium channel blockers, fentanyl, antibiotics, antiretrovirals, antifungals may be metabolized quicker, thus reducing their activity.

Gingko biloba – For patients who are older than 50 seeking a natural treatment for depression, gingko biloba may be a good choice. Take 240-320mg per day. In severe cases, it may be combined with Saint John's Wort, 5-HTP, or both but not with SSRIs or other Western antidepressants.

Ayahuasca – is an ancient plant medicine that grows naturally in the Amazon region of Central and South America. It is known as Mother Ayahuasca or Grandmother Ayahuasca, as it possesses the consciousness of the divine feminine Spirit. The plant grows like a snake-like vine. It contains an active chemical called N, N-Dimethyl-tryptamine, commonly referred to as DMT. Natives of the land report that upon connecting to the consciousness of the plant, (if you are curious about how to connect with the consciousness of plants, please read *The Secret Teachings of Plants: The Intelligence of the Heart in the Direct Perception of Nature* by Stephen Harrod Buhner), they were instructed to combine the vine with another plant called chakruna, which contains a chemical that prevents the rapid metabolism of DMT. When combined together and prepared ceremonially with intention and precision, the medicine can take the spiritual seeker on a journey out her body and into her own psyche, the Universe, and beyond. Many who have taken this ancient plant medicine report that it has helped them face the fear of death (my intuition tells me this is done by activating the death particle), meet

"God or Source," heal from their trauma, and relieve depression and anxiety.

Ceremonies are typically held in traditional style by sitting in a maloca/temple in a circle with an experienced shaman who pours the ayahuasca mixture and guides the ceremony. Traditional music called icaros is played throughout the ceremony. Shamans usually will meditate with the plant for 40 days or so (this is called a dieta) and are given the songs that are intimately connected to the consciousness of the plant. The music or the vibes can alter the way that the consciousness of the plant works with the seeker. The ceremonies usually last throughout the evening, and the medicine can last anywhere from 4 to 10 hours or so.

Mother Ayahuasca is not for everybody. Spiritual seekers often report that the plant will call them into a relationship, which once established seems to last lifetimes. It is vital that the plant be approached just as another human being would be approached. This means that one should bring a sense of humility, teachability, and respect when working with the plant. Just like a human, if approached with proper respect, it can be a tremendous teacher and heart opener.

It is vital to remember that intention is everything. The "why" behind the "what" is the driving force that brings purpose to each moment. Why are you seeking to work with Mother Ayahuasca? The plant will know. When first ingested, you will feel the plant working its way around your body, "checking you out." Like a good doctor, it will diagnose you, know why you have come to it for help, and based upon your energy and your openness, show you either what you need to give up, or what you're ready to see. It is also vital to remember that the plant can open up energy portals to the unseen world. Often times the navigator will have to travel through the density of the lower astral worlds, which some refer to as the lower fourth dimension, where a lot of different energies/entities reside. Some people get confused or lost in this realm. Therefore, it is essential that one work with a shaman or guide who has a pure heart and sufficient experience navigating these realms. The seeker is open and vulnerable during the journey, and the shaman is the guide who can help you when you get "stuck" or "lost" during the journey. There have also been many reports of shamans who are greedy for money, power, or lust. Please choose wisely with intuition and care. It is also important to understand the set, which refers to the immediate energy of the physical space, and setting, or the surrounding energy, of where you will be journeying. You want in a place with positive energy, with people you trust have your best interests in mind. I prefer the journey to be set up at home, in a comfortable, familiar space or in a relaxing, isolated place in nature.

This being said, Mother Ayahuasca has the ability to do in one night what a thousand therapy sessions can't do. It can light the divine spark. Once this divine spark in the heart is lit, the soul will know that there is more in this Universe and will be propelled onto a divine path of seeking higher levels of consciousness. It can show you that there is more to this Universe than just the third dimension. It can show you your beauty, your oneness with the Universe, your past lives, your Spirit Guides, and your purpose in life. It is a conscious, beautiful Spirit that can help you when worked with positive intentions and in the right set and setting. It has potential to help those with depression by biochemically altering the biochemistry of serotonin and dopamine and likely many other chemicals in the body. More importantly, it can change your attitude regarding yourself, this life, and God, thus activating the natural pharmacy in your body and brain, which is the best medicine. It is also showing tremendous potential to help victims of trauma. Some case studies report that the plant will provide space for the seeker to enter into their trauma, revisit it, forgive themselves and those involved, and reframe the trauma into a more positive emotional vibration.

It is vital that one is off of all SSRIs or serotonin-boosting medication for at least two weeks prior to any journey.

Please remember, working with Mother Ayahuasca is a calling, a privilege, and should be approached with careful research, respect, and humility. When I was first called to form a relationship with Mother Ayahuasca, the Universe opened up the pathway and it was a clear calling. Within moments of ingesting the plant, I could feel it moving throughout my body like a doctor, checking out each organ and cell. It was diagnosing me. Then I could feel the medicine moving throughout my GI system. When it had checked me out and found me to be "clean" enough, I was connected with a guide from my past life and crying tears of joy. I was then shown in the jungle, neon green lines coming out of me, into the tree I was meditating with. The neon green lines lit up the forest, connecting every piece of nature together in what appeared to be a colorful matrix of interconnection similar to the movie Avatar. In that moment, an intuitive knowing came over me that all of nature is connected in the invisible world and that we are never truly alone. That was a beautiful journey. However, there have been several journeys that have been difficult. One journey was akin to what some veterans of the medicine call the "white knuckle sleigh ride," where you are simply hanging on for dear life through the whole journey. I believe the medicine can sense your energy you bring to it, and so it is wise to approach the medicine when you are at a stable, clear place in your life, with a clear intention. I also highly recommend practicing rhythmic breathing prior to the journey, as it will be your anchor to reality and also help you be present and aware throughout your journey.

Please also note that some master yogis who can see the unseen world also report that chronic use of ayahuasca may have a detrimental effect on the kidneys. Although ayahuasca is not known to be chemically addictive, it seems that many seekers can become addicted to leaving their bodies as a way of escaping the third-dimensional reality. It can also be difficult to ground into the third dimension after journeying with the medicine, and the seeker should have a well-thought-out plan and community to help with proper integration after a ceremony. Integration is key. The plant can teach you tremendous lessons during the journey that can take a lifetime to integrate into the third dimension.

Please also note that ayahuasca is labeled as a schedule 1 "drug" by the United States government, despite the emerging evidence proving that it does have medical benefits. As it is currently illegal to use in the United States, one should plan on traveling to a country where it is legal.

For those who are interested in reading more about the medicine, please visit: reset.me/content-category/ayahuasca.

For those who feel called, I personally can vouch for the following center and guide: http://biopark.org/don-howard.html

Psilocybin (Magic Mushrooms) – Emerging studies have shown that magic mushrooms have significant promise to treat depression. (Malandra, 2011) Johns Hopkins has been doing research on the subject with a lot of positive findings. (Griffiths, et al., 2016)

Magic mushrooms have been used for many centuries, and some hypothesize that they could have been used even in biblical times. They contain the psychoactive compound psilocybin. Biochemically this medicine can form new neural pathways/synapses in the brain. This can lead to paradigm shifts in patterns of thinking to help seekers see themselves, others, their lives, and the world in a more truthful way that is in alignment with the energies of nature. It can sometimes be better than any doctor, as it can shift a person's attitude in one sitting. Some studies show that one proper experience with magic mushrooms can improve depressive symptoms quicker than any medication on the market. The effects can last up to three months or even longer. Studies have also shown that people who take magic mushrooms in a proper clinical trial often times cite that it was among the most "spiritual" experiences of their lives. There are indications that it can help shift one's entire worldview or belief system in one sitting. This is extraordinary. By shifting one's belief system, it shifts the thought patterns, which shifts the emotional vibrations, which affects cell permeability, which leads to different genetic expression, which leads to proteins and hormones that are in alignment with the belief system. Not to mention that the medicine is likely also biochemically altering the neurotransmitter system directly to bring it into balance with nature.

Many are introduced to magic mushrooms in non-ceremonial settings such as parties. This can sometimes lead to a "bad trip." The mushrooms can open up energetic portals to the unseen world; therefore, it is vital to take them in a contained environment surrounded by the type of energy you want to experience. Otherwise it may lead to an experience of not knowing what or whose energy the seeker is experiencing. Just like ayahuasca, the set, setting, and intention are key to the experience. Most first-time seekers might want to have a trusted friend or guide sit with them to hold space and ensure safety.

Most advanced, conscious seekers only use the medicine with clear, positive intention. Often times this can be in a contained, safe environment in nature with an intention to connect with nature. Some advanced psychonauts like to experience the medicine by making a playlist with the type of music/energy they want to experience. Once the playlist is set, they put a journal next to their space. They can then carefully research the dosing and preparation by visiting a site such as erowid.org. Once they have a clear intention, an open space, and a solid music playlist, they ingest the medicine. Then they can lie down, cover their eyes with a blindfold, turn on the music, and start breathing rhythmically (inhale for four seconds, hold for seven seconds, exhale for eight seconds, or another rhythmic breath, such as box breathing) then simply let go and let the medicine take them into their own psyche. This often leads to profound realizations, as the medicine will often honor one's intentions.

Magic mushrooms hold potential to be helpful for multiple psychiatric conditions, including depression, anxiety, and trauma, and they can also be helpful with geriatric patients as they transition to the "other side."

Please note that, according to the US government, at this time magic mushrooms are considered an illegal substance with no medical benefits. However, the conscious community knows from experience that the medicine can be beneficial, and promising scientific research is being done.

Ketamine – is an up and coming treatment for major depression. It seems to work to quickly to alleviate acute depressive symptoms. Some studies show that it works quicker than antidepressant medications and seems to be better tolerated by most patients. The effects can take place within 24 hours. Some studies show that the effects can be prolonged and help the brain form new neural connections. However, the treatment can be expensive, and one needs to see the doctor on a regular basis to receive injections or intramuscular shots. The FDA has just approved a new intranasal spray called esketamine. However, it is not considered a primary treatment for depression. Currently, it is only recommended it be used when a patient has failed two trials of antidepressants and is treatment resistant.

If you are considering ketamine as a treatment for depression, it is recommended you find a trustworthy doctor to work with. Please remember ketamine is not a cure-all. It can help alleviate symptoms, but there must be other treatments that target the root cause of the depression to go along with it.

Those in the spiritual community sometimes refer to ketamine as "God juice." If done in the right set and setting, with the right intention, it can facilitate "ego death," where the mind is quiet, and help the seeker realize that there is more to life than just what experiences in the daily third-dimensional realm. This profound experience can often lead to a renewed sense of joy, purpose, and hope.

If I had a family member who did not want to try psilocybin and did not want Western medications, I would definitely recommend a trial of ketamine for acute depression.

Essential Oils

Scent is an underrated medicine. Inhaling essential oils may be a quick, natural way to relieve depressive symptoms and improve energy. Essential oils are ancient medicines, which are now being revived as Mother Nature is revealing more of her healing properties as consciousness is rising.

Bergamot – may create feelings of joy and increase energy by having a positive effect on circulation in the blood.

Lavender – helps soothe the nervous system and may be helpful for anxiety and depression.

Ylang ylang – may be helpful for those with stress-induced depressive symptoms, as this scent can lower stress responses and be a mild sedative.

Roman Chamomile – may help lower anxiety and depressive symptoms.

For depressive symptoms, I recommend taking 1 drop of lavender oil, ylang ylang oil, and bergamot oil and rubbing it into your hands. Cup your mouth and nose, breathe in the oil slowly, and let it permeate into your circulation. It is best to take three slow, long, deep, rhythmic breaths while inhaling and setting a positive intention. Then, rub the oils on your stomach and then your feet.

F. 21-Day Program to Kick Depression

I have created a 21-day program to kick depression. In this program you will receive a link to a 21-minute video to change your entire energetic frequency. This video was specifically created to incorporate movement and breath and to change your energetic frequency from low-vibration emotions to high-vibration emotions. Not only will you receive the video, but you will also receive specific recommendations to incorporate into your life during your 21-day challenge to a happier, healthier you.

Please follow your intuition and sign up if you so feel called. Here's a link to the program: www.21days.thespiritualpsychiatrist.com

CHAPTER 5:
BIPOLAR DISORDER

A. A Spiritual Paradigm of Bipolar Disorder

Bipolar disorder, from an energetic perspective, is when the brain becomes overwhelmed with suppressed and repressed emotions and thoughts. This leads to a sequence of sporadic and scattered brain wave fluctuations, which manifest on the physical plane as manic symptoms, often followed by a depressive crash when the energy has dissipated. It is often precipitated or preceded by a highly charged emotional experience or event, which triggers a cascade of energetic fluctuations leading to the classic symptoms. Often times for the experiencer, mania is a spiritual or highly energetic experience. During the event, the brain is overwhelmed with energy and the experiencer cannot separate his/her ego identity from his/her energetic/spiritual identity (the discerning, wise Higher Self). This is why often times the experiencer feels like nobody can understand them and is not able to receive constructive criticism from people who truly care for them; they are only able to perceive from their ego/separate identity. They are stuck in their ego identity where suppressed and repressed emotions and energies rush to the brain, causing racing thoughts and lack of sleep, which feeds the cycle of symptoms.

When someone is experiencing mania, the best medicine is sleep. Sleep will help shift the energies from the brain and clear out the subconscious thought patterns, which are overwhelming the system. However, for someone experiencing mania, it is nearly impossible to sleep. For the body to sleep, the mind must fall asleep. For the person experiencing mania, it is nearly impossible to move the energy from the mind to the rest of the body without proper training in breathwork and/or meditation. Because the ego identity is often in control, the person experiencing mania will often times feel like they can accomplish anything and like they are invincible. They will start many projects and speak in a grandiose manner. Any type of criticism will be looked upon as someone trying to suppress their dreams and goals and will lead to sadness, which will often times be transmuted into anger and irritability. Manic symptoms can actually be productive for the person who is conscious and able to ground the energy into the physical plane and distribute the energy. Most often in manic episodes, the amygdala is shut off, and the person is fearless and does not feel any resistance towards their goals and aspirations. This often leads to giving away money, possessions, and acting "out of character." If they are able to ground this energy into the physical, they will be able to move forward with their dreams and accomplish many projects, which they previously would have been afraid to do.

Manic patients will experience unusual bursts of energy, which often come with a sense of confidence and invincibility. Because manic symptoms do not fit in with what modern society has deemed acceptable, manic people are usually unable to function in normal society and pressured to be placed into a psychiatric hospital where their energy can be contained, restrained, and quelled. Many manic patients will often over-expend their energy resources during their episodes. They will often times feel sad that none of their loved ones are resonating with their energy and don't seem to be understanding them. This sadness will often times be transmuted into anger, and they can act from this anger and say and do things that hurt the people around them, often causing permanent damage. It is often highly sensitive and spiritually minded people who experience mania because they are more emotionally sensitive to energy and often times take on the energy of those around them. They have also, for most of their life, been taught to suppress the energies of their dreams because it was not "acceptable" to their parents' or societies' conditioning. These energies often come to the surface all at once during a manic episode.

It is essential for those experiencing mania to have a supportive community who do not criticize them but understand them. They need loving family or friends who can speak to them with an intention of care and love and encourage them to sleep and ground themselves. Friends and family who push them into psychiatric hospitals often damage these relationships. This does not mean that the family or friends should not speak their truth; it just means that instead of communicating with an intention to argue, defend, or attack, that all communication be held with the intention of listening, communicating, resonating, and understanding. All conversations should be held in a calm, open manner with the intention of understanding. There is no prize for being "right" or "winning" the conversation. The manic patient is in a state of attacking or defending, so it is vital to approach them with the right tone and loving intention. Any perceived attack will be met with defense, which will lead to anger, resentment, and more hurt. Once effective communication is had, it would be wise to either agree to disagree and/or to compromise. If a manic patient truly feels loved, not judged, and supported, they may even agree to sleep because of the intention they feel from the other party. Although they may not agree that they need sleep, they will try because they can feel the honest, loving intention. In extreme cases, where the manic patient is out of control and in danger of hurting themselves or others, it may be wise to call on outside forces, such as the police, and the experiencer may be placed in a psychiatric hospital, where they will be given medications and forced to calm down and numb their frontal lobes. Although it is not the ideal place, psychiatric hospitals are effective at providing a safe place for the manic patient to be forced to take medications and come back "down to earth." This is the best the "system" has to offer currently.

B. My Testimony of Manic Experiences

In my journey thus far, I have experienced what modern psychiatry would label as two "manic" episodes. The first episode occurred after I had been repressing my heart and its feelings for over six years. I was in a relationship with my best friend, and deep inside my heart I knew she was a friend and not my wife. However, because of fear and conditioning, I chose to stay in the relationship for six years, the whole time ignoring the promptings and intelligence of my heart. This suppressed a lot of feelings and pent up emotions. Often, I felt "bad" or "guilty," and these feelings prompted me to stay in the relationship and not speak my truth. I proposed and flew to Las Vegas for a bachelor party with 16 of my finest "party friends." Looking back, there were several key events that led to my mania. The first was mixing a lack of sleep with many chemical substances, as is often the case with most manic episodes. Another contributing factor was the high energy of the club scenes in Las Vegas, as well being the center of attention at my party. This accumulation of energy and lack of cleansing the mind through sleep led to an argument with one of my friends. I am a highly sensitive individual and do not take fights well. The energy of sadness turned quickly to anger. This led to a series of arguments with other friends, which quickly turned into a full-blown manic episode and me calling off the wedding in a heated rage. My mind was racing, I was lacking sleep, I was grandiose, and many of the repressed feelings were coming to surface. To most people, it may sound strange, but it was a highly spiritual experience for me. I felt many repressed feelings and emotions coming to surface. I felt I was speaking my truth on matters, which previously I had held in. I felt nobody understood me, except for God. At some points I even felt I was feeling what it would feel like to be Jesus in Gethsemane. Alone, betrayed by his friends and family, with nobody understanding Him, and all that was left was faith and trust in God.

My friends and family at that time took the stance of treating me like a "crazy" person to no fault of their own. I was operating from my ego, and they were worried about me. They conspired with my fiancée to cut off my funds. I had no money, no food, and at that time what I perceived to be no family or friends. My friends flew in for the wedding but were treating me like a mental patient. They refused to do anything with me except sit around me and look at me as if I was crazy and whisper behind my back. There was a strange energy of withholding what they really felt, which led to even more sadness, which fed the anger. My family members told my friends I was not normal and conspired together to get me admitted to a psychiatric hospital. I refused because I knew exactly what would happen there. I would be given shots and numbed with toxic medications. I ended up getting through the manic episode by myself but was left empty, alone, and broken.

In hindsight, it was one of the most necessary and fortuitous events that could have happened to me. I realize that sometimes the Universe works in mysterious ways and that the Universe was working for me and not against me. I realized that because I was ignoring the promptings of my heart for so long, the Universe had to rip apart the chords that I refused to let go of that were not in my best interest long term. It prevented me from a marriage, which would not have been in alignment with my purpose during this incarnation. And only through this experience and hitting "rock bottom" I was able to discover a yoga studio across from my apartment and reconnect with my Higher Self.

Through this experience, I was able to find the gift of breathing and awareness and reconnect with my Higher Self, who I was running away from for the past seven years. It was a tragic experience, which turned into a blessing. The experience also filtered out my friends for me. After the experience, the friends who were not in alignment with my higher purpose naturally and gradually fell away. The experience also helped me to begin to have the courage to start expressing who I truly was.

My second experience with mania occurred after my conscious "awakening." It was truly different than the first experience, as I was conscious of what was happening. It again occurred after a breakup with a girlfriend, who I was convinced was "the one." After the breakup, I was left picking up the pieces. I was consciously sad and grieving. This sadness turned into anger, which I channeled into my breathwork practices. All energy can be transmuted. Sadness can turn into anger, which can then be transmuted into drive and devotion. But it all starts with being conscious of one's own energy, thoughts, actions, and behavior, which always returns to being conscious of the breath. I channeled the manic, angry energy into learning about and practicing breathwork with an intention to eventually teach others about the gift of the breath of life. I consciously used breathing techniques to try to help me channel the energy out of the mind and into the rest of my body. I used herbs and breathing techniques to help me fall asleep. Although I was "manic," I did not end up causing permanent damage to my friends and family because I was able to go through the experience consciously. Spirituality simply means consciousness or awareness and is always tied back to being aware of the breath. Conscious "mania" is not an easy process to go through but when navigated with loving awareness can become a lesson, a blessing, and an opportunity for continued growth in consciousness.

C. Western Psychiatry and Bipolar Disorder

In modern Western psychiatry, bipolar disorder is labeled as a "distinct period of abnormally and persistently elevated, expansive, or irritable mood." The episode must last at least a week. The mood must have at least three of the following symptoms: high self-esteem/grandiosity, decreased need for sleep, rapid speech, flight of ideas, getting easily distracted, an increased interest in goals or activities, psychomotor agitation (pacing, hand wringing, etc.), and increase in goal-oriented activities (Diagnostic and Statistical Manual of Mental Disorders, Fifth Edition, 2013). These criteria come from the Psychiatrist's bible, The *DSM-5*, and are based on psychiatrists' opinions and often biased and hand-selected research articles sponsored by pharmaceutical companies.

Bipolar disorder is often misdiagnosed by psychiatrists who are in a rush and don't have adequate time to fully understand the circumstances that led to the "manic" episode. Most psychiatrists will rush through a checklist of symptoms, then diagnose you with bipolar disorder at the end of the interview and place you on medications, which you are supposed to take for the rest of your life. This is great for the pharmaceutical companies that have convinced society to believe that there is no cure and that it is simply a chemical imbalance that is to blame for the symptoms. Also, when one takes these medications consistently for a period of time, it is nearly impossible to get off the medications without having rebound symptoms. Thus, the patient has to keep going back to the doctor for medications and continue purchasing the pills, which benefits the pharmaceutical companies. If a patient wants to get off the medication, their body will suffer the rebound symptoms if not done with intentional care and research.

The usual medications for bipolar disorder include medications that are often also used for seizure disorders, such as Depakote, carbamazepine, and Lamictal. Another common medication is lithium. From my clinical perspective, I have found that a low dose of lithium can often be beneficial for someone seeking a natural way to cope with his or her mood fluctuations. It is a natural salt and at low dosages does not seem to cause long-term side effects. However, when used at higher dosages for a long period of time, it often causes kidney failure, which can be difficult or impossible to reverse. Nobody knows the exact mechanism of anti-seizure medications, but from my clinical practice, they seem to numb down the energies in the brain, causing the person to be more "calm," "mellow," and "sluggish." Though these medications may temporarily subdue manic symptoms, they by no means are actually dealing with the cause of the energy fluctuations, which means the symptoms can reappear. It also means that the suppressed feelings and emotions continue to accumulate, which may lead to an even greater frequency/energetic mania in the near future. These medications often times also cause weight gain and drowsiness and can be toxic to the person taking them long term. They also subdue creative energy and make it difficult for anybody to pursue their creative life purpose. The patient often times becomes dependent on the medication and forms not only a physical and chemical but also an emotional addiction to the medication and starts to feel that they cannot be "normal" without the medications. Their family members, often times conditioned by mass media, will also take on the opinion that their son/daughter/friend has to take their medications in order to be "normal." The whole time the creative uniqueness of the patient is being stifled, thereby repressing/suppressing even more energies, which often times leads to a cycle of repetitive, periodic manic episodes and hospitalizations. This often turns into regular trips to the inpatient psychiatric hospital and a merry-go-round of trying different psychiatric medications throughout one's life while never even thinking that there is a cure or other natural modalities that may help balance and ground the energies. The tragedy occurs when the experiencer starts to see him or herself as damaged, weird, and cut off from society at large. This leads to fear and isolation, which often leads to further disease and sometimes even losing all hope and suicide.

For acute manic symptoms, benzodiazepines can be very effective at calming down the mind and putting a patient to sleep. Benzodiazepines such as Xanax, Ativan, valium, and Klonopin can be effectively used as a short-term aid. These medications work on the GABA receptors in the brain, which help calm down the brain and thus the body. It can also help an experiencer of mania get much needed sleep. Using benzodiazepines, however, is not a great long-term solution, as they are addictive, deadly in overdose, and stop working if used excessively. Tolerance is easily built, so they are best used for acute, periodic conditions to help instantly calm down a patient, such as during plane trips or manic episodes. These are not good drugs to use daily but can be used effectively to calm down acute manic symptoms. If used only for a short period of time, with a specific intention in mind, and with a trustworthy, caring doctor, benzodiazepines can help tremendously in acute mania without causing long-term side effects.

D. Alternative Treatments for Bipolar Disorder

Diet

Identify and avoid allergenic foods. Try avoiding caffeine for a 30-day period to see if this helps symptoms.

A daily nutritional supplement that contains all of the daily essential nutrients the human body needs and has scientific research to back it up can be helpful for bipolar disorder as well as other mental health conditions. Hardy Nutritionals carries such a product called "Daily Essential Nutrients," which has hundreds of great product reviews.

Magnesium – 300-600mg/day.

N-Acetylcysteine – 1,000mg twice a day.

Fish Oil – Find dosages/brands that supply 9.6g/day of omega-3 fatty acids in adults and in children, 1.3-4.3g/day of omega-3 fatty acids.

L-Tryptophan – For bipolar 1 disorder, 6-12 g/day; For bipolar 2 disorder II, 2-3 g/day.

Chromium – 400-600 micrograms/day, especially for patients who crave carbohydrates.

Foot Treatments

Souls who are in an acute manic episode need to bring the energy down from the brain and ground it into their feet and the earth. Foot reflexology from a trusted energetic energy worker can be a good way to move the energy from the overactive mind down into the feet.

Making contact with the ground with the bare feet is also a good way to ground the energy. If the person who is in an acute manic episode refuses to sleep, however he is open to nature therapy, it would be a good idea to take a barefoot hike in a quiet area with a trusted friend who can monitor him. Contact with the earth's floor will connect the energy and frequency of the earth. Science is slowly starting to realize that the whole body can be healed simply through the feet. Walking barefoot will give you free acupressure and heal your body. By walking barefoot on the earth, you are pressing in on pressure points, which are connected via energy channels and meridians to your entire body.

It is a great idea for everybody to spend at least 10 to 15 minutes each day walking barefoot on the ground, as it will decrease inflammation and help every dis-ease condition.

Another way to ground the energy is to soak the feet each evening in a bucket filled with warm/hot water, a few drops of eucalyptus essential oil, as well as some sea salt. This can not only help ground energy but get one ready for deep sleep.

Breathwork for Bipolar Disorder

A person who is in an acute manic episode will be breathing in an erratic manner. If you watch their breath, you will be able to see that the inhales and exhales have no rhythm and are erratic, which means the mind is leading the way and that the brain waves are correspondingly erratic and irregular.

I would highly recommend trying to get the person to breathe in a calm, rhythmic manner. The 4/7/8 breath as well as the box breath are good breaths to try in these situations.

Please see description of these breaths in the next chapter on Anxiety under the Breathwork subsection.

CHAPTER 6:
ANXIETY

A. An Energetic Paradigm of Anxiety

Anxiety is when one's awareness is focused on past or future events, leading to the false feeling that one is in danger, which is manifested by an erratic breathing pattern, which is mirroring the erratic brain waves, which are reflecting the subconscious or conscious mind, which is running on programming or conditioning from a trauma or false belief system. It can be treated instantaneously by calming the breath so it is slow and rhythmic and sinking into the present moment. You'll never find anyone who is anxious but breathing in a calm, relaxed, rhythmic, "normal" manner. This is because the brain waves mirror the breathing rate. **The breath will either follow the mind or the mind will follow the breath.** When one is anxious, the mind is leading the way. The mind is either focused on the past or worrying about the future, fearing something bad is going to happen that hasn't happened yet. When the mind is stuck on such a thought, one loses all sense of the breath and forgets that they are not their thoughts. This leads to an erratic breathing pattern and disharmonious brain wave frequencies, leading to an erratic heart rate, and thus manifesting as what one calls "anxiety."

Most city dwellers' nervous systems are fried. From the moment they wake up, they are in a rush, worrying about the day ahead, on the "go," and stuck in beta brain waves, which activate the sympathetic nervous system. Most go through a subconscious routine of checking email, brushing teeth, rushing to work, etc. Rarely do they pause to be still and come into still awareness of the breath.

When one is able to focus on the movement of breath within the body, conscious alchemy happens. Attention to the movement of breath begins a process of clearing and purifying the meridian channels through which energy runs. On an emotional level, the brain waves will start synchronizing to the rhythm and rate of the breath. The quickest way to appease anxiety is to pause and sense the movement of breath within the body. It is easy to identify anyone who is anxious by the way they breathe. A person who is anxious will have a shallow, erratic breath pattern. A person who is calm will be breathing in relaxed, quiet, and rhythmic breath pattern.

Beta brain waves correspond to the state of being where the breath is matching the activity of the thoughts. It is on the go, in a rush, and activates the sympathetic nervous system. The sympathetic nervous system is the part of our nervous system that is in fight or flight and activates when the body senses it is in a rush or in danger. It is also the reactionary state where one runs mostly on subconscious programming. It activates the stress hormones, which leads to all kinds of inflammation and dis-ease. Our bodies were not meant to be in overdrive all day. So, in order to switch it off and to enter in a rest and relaxation mode, one simply needs to stop and take three slow, long, rhythmic deep breaths then continue to breathe in a rhythmic fashion. The brain waves will start to entrain into the rhythm of the breath, and you will slowly drop into an alpha brain wave state. In this state, you will be able to observe your mind, rather than be controlled by it. You will be able to focus and concentrate on whatever you choose to place your attention on and be able to actually get intelligent, creative work done. You may even be able to see the subconscious programming running and override it by returning your attention to the breath and the present moment.

When deep relaxation is desired, you can continue in a rhythmic breathing pattern and enter into theta brain waves, where you are open, suggestible, and the subconscious programming can not only be easily identified but new programming software can be inserted. This will be discussed more in later chapters.

So, the key to overcoming anxiety is to allow the breath to lead the way rather than the mind. When the breath is slow, you can actually start observing your thoughts without identifying with them.

I highly recommend reading Michael Singer's book entitled *The Untethered Soul*. Michael has a beautiful way of explaining the processes of the mind in such a simple way that anyone can understand it. If you can actually learn that you are not your thoughts, you are on your way to freeing yourself from chronic anxiety. Your thoughts are running on a set of programmed, conditioned belief systems and patterns. The origin of these thoughts can usually be traced back to early childhood, generational, societal, and karmic conditioning. The programming is not your fault but has been subconsciously engrained into your mind through television programming, ads on the street, social media, parents, religion, school, etc. Once you are aware of the programming, you can then start restructuring, reframing, deleting, or adding new programming. It is vital for anyone suffering from anxiety to actually learn how to breathe. Just like with anything in life, in order to learn something, someone has to teach you and you have to practice. I will offer a few breathing techniques at the end of this chapter that will be a good way to start learning.

It is important also here to mention the role that fear plays in anxiety. The amygdala is a part of the brain that scientists believe is responsible for the fear response. The root of fear is the belief in separation. This means that as soon as someone believes that they are different (race, religion, gender, socioeconomic status, etc.) from somebody else, there is a sense of fear or separation. The amygdala, as soon as it senses that there is someone else who is different and may be a threat, reacts and triggers the sympathetic nervous system to automatically go into a mode of reaction, survival, and often times anxiety. The body senses through the amygdala that you are in danger or that something bad is going to happen. When you start focusing on the possibility of bad things happening, you are feeding the energy behind the idea and increasing the chances that the event will actually occur. Thoughts are energy forms that come and go. You can think of them as clouds coming and going above your head. So, when a thought enters into your mind, you can simply observe it as if looking at a cloud—watch it, acknowledge it, let it come and go, and return your attention to your breath.

Most people have so much negative emotion attached to their trauma or cause of anxiety that when it appears, they do not have the ability to sit with it, observe it, and actually figure out what is at the root of the feeling. Most people will panic and feel as if they should suppress the feeling, avoid it, distract themselves from it, or punish themselves for having the feeling. This will only exacerbate the anxiety or trauma. In these types of situations, it is very important to find a practice or person who is able to hold space for you, calm you down, and enable you to feel safe enough to explore the feeling. Your Higher Self already knows the root cause of the feeling. The problem is most people are so busy thinking that they get lost in circular and repetitive patterns of mind and are not able to quiet it enough to allow the Higher Self to reveal what is going on. This is why learning how to breathe is so important. It is the quickest way to calm and quiet the mind so that you can actually learn how to listen to your intuition or Higher Self. If you do not have the tools or know how to sit with your Higher Self, it's important to find a good therapist, friend, or mentor who can guide you into relaxation and guide you into the root cause of the anxiety so that you can address it at the root. This person should be someone you trust who doesn't care whether or not you like them. It should be someone who loves you enough to only care about your liberation from your suffering. When you find someone like this, hold onto them and accept their help if it is offered.

Anxiety can also be triggered by environmental cues, which trigger the fear response in the amygdala. These cues are often associated with past traumas or negative events and often times are not easily noticed. For example, if you had a bad breakup with your girlfriend, and unresolved low-vibration emotions surrounding the breakup, any environmental cue that reminds you of your girlfriend can trigger anxiety or fear. It can be as simple as a scent that re-minds you of your ex-girlfriend. Once again, in these situations it is important to not avoid the emotion but to let it flow through your meridians and out of your system. Do not suppress the feeling, or the energy may get stuck. It is best to actually go into the feeling with healthy curiosity to explore the origin of where it is coming from and what it is trying to teach you. Everything is a lesson, a blessing, or an opportunity if you think it is.

Remember, you are not your thoughts, feelings, trauma, or past experiences. Thoughts will come and go. Feelings will come and go. Experiences will come and go. Who is the one that is always watching? You! The Higher Self. You are not the clouds (thought energy forms) but you are the sky. You are always there and always have been there and always will be there. So, remember, no matter how severe the anxiety, or trauma, it will pass. Stop, feel, find your breath, and as soon as you realize you've lost awareness of your breath, return to your breath. It is your best friend. It is the "sky." It is the biological remembrance of who you are behind the anxiety and trauma. And please, please learn how to breathe.

B. Westernized Perspective of Anxiety:

In Western psychiatry, anxiety is usually categorized into general-ized anxiety, post-traumatic stress disorder, social anxiety, and panic disorder. Generalized anxiety is when you experience anxiety most days for longer than one month. Post-traumatic stress disor-der is when you experienced or witnessed a life-threatening event and continue to replay it back through nightmares and flashbacks and feel a sense of anxiety, hyperarousal, and fidgetiness, all the time fearing that the traumatic event will reoccur. Social anxiety means you are so caught in your thoughts, concerned with what other people think, or scared of others that you shrink in social sit-uations and end up isolating rather than connecting. Panic disorder is when your nervous system becomes overwhelmed with a per-ceived threat, substance, subconscious memory, or situation that you get lost into it. A person in a panic attack often times loses sight of their breath and their heart rate becomes rapid. One can feel an overwhelming sensation that they are going to die or something terrible is going to happen. The *DSM-5* categorizes these into a specific checklist of symptoms. Panic disorders can also sometimes arise spontaneously or "out of the blue." In my opinion, this is usually suppressed feelings or memories, subconscious or unconscious, coming to surface to be cleared. Search the *DSM-5* online to see what psychiatrists have labeled and created as anxiety disorders.

C. Western Treatment of Anxiety

If you go see a psychiatrist for anxiety, you likely will be placed on psychiatric medications.

Benzodiazepines, such as Ativan, Xanax, valium, Restoril, etc., are often used for short-term anxiety and panic attacks. This class of medications works on the GABA receptors in the brain, which are responsible for calming down the nervous system. They usually work well in the beginning by sedating you enough so that you are not anxious anymore. You can also sometimes feel a sense of euphoria as if you were drunk or high. However, over a period of time, if used chronically, the body builds tolerance to these medications, and you may become physically and mentally addicted to them. It is a good way to "check out." You may feel like you are tired and sleepy and will not be able to focus. This class of medications is widely abused by people who aren't able to actually cope with what's really going on and decide they would rather check out and be numb instead of actually dealing with the root cause of what's going on. They can also cause memory impairment because nothing is being registered, as you are not aware or attentive when on these medications. For the elderly, benzodiazepines can increase the chances or exacerbate the symptoms of dementia. These medications, when taken in large quantities, can also kill you by stopping your breathing. Many people attempt suicide by overdosing on benzodiazepines.

If you are suffering from chronic or daily anxiety, you will likely be placed on a SSRI medication, as described in the Chapter 4 on Depression. These medications are used for almost every psychiatric condition because they are good at numbing you and shutting down energy centers of the body, thereby decreasing most "negative" and "positive" feelings. Nobody knows exactly how SSRIs work, but the hypothesis is that they alter serotonin levels. This can be a good way to "numb" yourself over a long period of time and continue to be able to live your "normal" life while continuing to allow whatever is actually causing your anxiety to continue. Eventually, the body will adjust, and you will likely need to add another medication, increase the dose, or try a different psychiatric medication. Most psychiatrists, to no fault of their own, don't have time to actually talk with you and address the root cause of what's going on. They are simply following a system that has trained them to ask questions in search of which medication to prescribe, rather than ask questions to find a cure.

Other medications that may be tried include Neurontin and Seroquel, as well as another class of antidepressants called SNRIs (serotonin-norepinephrine reuptake inhibitors). They, too, may temporarily help the anxiety but do not address what's really going on. They also have side effects and will likely stop working once the body adjusts.

D. My Testimony of Anxiety

At one point in my life's journey I could've been labeled with post-traumatic stress disorder, generalized anxiety disorder, social anxiety disorder, and panic disorder. The PTSD symptoms mainly stemmed from an idea being subconsciously ingrained from a young age that sex was "bad." My parents never talked about it. The only time I ever remember my mother talking to me about it was when she was lecturing me about how masturbation was a terrible sin. I grew up reading books that told me that if I had sex before marriage, I would be like a half-eaten, rotten apple for my future wife instead of a pure, wholesome apple. So, I never talked about it, or thought about it, until one day my oldest brother introduced me to porn. I was in junior high at the time. I remember watching it and feeling a weird sensation of immediate pleasure, but always had severe guilt after watching it. So, I avoided all things sexual. Deep in my subconscious, I was forming a belief that sex was bad unless you were married and did it in secret. It was never to be talked about or discussed in public. At the age of 21, I had still yet to experience my first real kiss. I was saving myself to be pure for my future wife. Then at the age of 21, I became frustrated with the "lukewarmness" of the church and prayed to God, telling Him that I was going to go explore the world and I would be back, asking Him to wait for me. I started to explore all things sexual and lost my virginity shortly thereafter. After each sexual experience, I had tremendous feelings of guilt but at the same time was enthralled and curious by the pleasure of the experience. I then went into a full-blown party stage with a lot of alcohol and women involved. In this stage, I received a lot of love from my party friends for being "smooth" with women, especially when I was intoxicated. Although the primary intent was fun, I remember each Monday morning, sitting on the toilet with the "alki/Hershey squirts" (alcohol induced diarrhea) feeling a tremendous amount of guilt and shame about the lifestyle I was living. This whole time, I felt like I needed to return to church, reading the Bible and being a good Christian boy, in order to feel whole again (also subconscious programming from childhood).

After partying hard for seven years, I was left in an unhealthy state mentally, physically, and spiritually. I decided to try to return to the church. This led to a severe amount of guilt, shame, and fear. Everywhere I went, I felt like I was tainted, dirty, and sinful. I had severe social anxiety. Anytime I ran across a female, I felt guilt. I couldn't make eye contact. It became so severe that anytime I was around a female, I would avoid contact. This became very traumatic for me. Even when I was alone, I would feel guilty and ashamed of my past. All the while, there was a natural attraction to females, which most men have, as they are beautiful, sacred beings. This led me to a few panic attacks on a few occasions where I literally felt I was going to die.

These symptoms still rear their ugly heads occasionally, but now I know consciously that I am not sinful and where these symptoms originate. To heal my anxiety, I started to learn yoga. After yoga class, in the silence, I could start to see where the conditioning and programming around sex came from. The core beliefs that I was taught as a child were the root cause of the thoughts that I was bad and that I was sinful. I went to the Amazon and into a deep exploration of plant medicine, which opened my heart to myself and gave me further insight. I was slowly starting to piece together the puzzle of what was actually causing my anxiety. Ibogaine was a very powerful plant, which showed me exactly where the subconscious programming had come from and also "defragmented" the computer of my mind so that it could have more space for my creative endeavors.

Then, through my spiritual exploration, I was able to start changing the low-frequency emotions associated with the trauma. I was able to start associating these experiences with profound compassion, grace, and love instead of guilt, shame, and fear. Instead of seeing myself as a sinner and bad, I started to see that every experience I had was an opportunity for growth—an opportunity to learn and overcome these low-frequency emotions so that I could help other people suffering from the same type of symptoms. I started reframing my core beliefs and letting go of limiting beliefs to the point now where I know and believe that all human beings, including myself, are limitless. I started to have compassion for myself. When the thoughts and feelings of the past arose, I started to be able to sit with them, go deep into them, and explore them with healthy curiosity. Most of all, I learned how to breathe. I learned how to be present. I learned how to let go. And I learned that everything is a lesson, a blessing, and an opportunity if I think it is.

These days, I have evolved to a place where I'm fine with anxiety. I realize it's a feeling and not who I am. I am able to sit with it, honor it, and take time for myself when needed. It doesn't dictate my life any longer. It still occasionally limits my interactions, but I am conscious of it and am healing it day by day.

You too can overcome your anxiety, but the root cause is not a chemical imbalance that you were born with, and awareness is the first step of change.

The root cause stems from a frantic amygdala that thinks you're in danger constantly or thinks something bad is going to happen because of the programming and conditioning you have been blessed with during this lifetime. It is a blessing because you can overcome it and help others with it. The most powerful tool is right below your nose; it's free and abundant. The breath will either follow the mind or the mind will follow the breath. As we learn how to breathe, we will be able to calm ourselves, approach our anxiety with healthy curiosity, and start exploring where it comes from and what it is trying to teach us. Once we've discovered the root cause, we can start charging the trauma or anxiety with compassion, grace, and love rather than the low-frequency emotions currently associated with it. The breath will allow you to be calm enough to pierce through the low-vibration emotions surrounding the trauma or anxiety, explore them, and start restructuring, deleting, and re-framing the core belief systems that cause the anxiety. Then, once that work has been dealt with, we can simply notice the thoughts, and they will start to dissipate even before they manifest on the physical plane. Then we can watch our thoughts come and go and simply drop into the beauty and subtleties of the present moment. The more aware one is of the subtleties of the present moment, the more one is aware of God, for God is in All that is.

E. Natural Ways to Combat Anxiety

Breathwork

Please note that the most typical biochemical disturbance in people with anxiety is noted as an elevated blood lactate level, which is the final product in the breakdown of blood sugar (glucose) when there is a lack of oxygen. Therefore, for immediate relief of anxiety, the most acute and effective treatment is to find a calm, rhythmic breath, improve oxygenation, and establish calm brain waves, which will lead to a calm heart rate.

Daily breathwork is the best treatment for anxiety. Anxiety usually occurs when our thoughts are dwelling in a future worry or a past event or trauma. It can also be subconsciously triggered by an outside stimulus, which reminds our unconscious brains of a stressful event. Remember, the breath will either follow the mind or the mind will follow the breath. If one is conscious, they will notice that the breath is erratically following the mind when one is anxious. The goal is to let the breath lead the way, thereby establishing calm brain waves, and coming into the present moment where there is no anxiety.

The following are breathwork techniques that are proven to work for acute anxiety.

Box Breathing – There are four parts of a full respiration: inhale, hold in, exhale, and hold out. A box has four sides, and thus this breath is called the box breath. Inhale for four seconds. Hold for four seconds. Exhale for four seconds. Hold out for four seconds. The four seconds is variable and can be adjusted to fit the current capacity of each person. The breath should be breathed calmly, without rush, as if savoring the breath. This breath can be done anywhere and will rapidly establish a calm internal state. Please utilize this technique frequently. My recommendation is to start by practicing for two minutes five times a day, 10 minutes in total.

This breath has been utilized by Navy Seals whenever they need a calm internal state. It works. Mark Divine is a former Navy Seal who is a big proponent of this breath. Please google search Mark Divine and you can find some of his work. You can also find videos online for practicing this breath.

4/7/8 Breath – This is a simple ancient breathing technique that really works. Gently position the tongue so the tip of the tongue gently touches the upper palate behind the top teeth. Inhale calmly through the nose for four seconds. Hold the breath for seven seconds. Exhale softly and gently for eight seconds, either through the mouth or through the nose. The longer exhales soothe the nervous system and activate the parasympathetic nervous system. We are made of at least 70% water. When we inhale, we are moving the internal water, as most water is in the abdominal cavity. On the inhale, imagine a wave at the ocean gently building up for four seconds. On the exhale, imagine a wave crashing gently for eight seconds. Remember that when a wave crashes, there is no force involved. This is also true with this exhale. The exhale should simply be releasing the diaphragm and watching nature take its course as the air is naturally expelled in a slow, calm fashion. We are made of water, and when you inhale, build up the internal waters with the movement of the diaphragm, and when you exhale, simply allow the wave to crash.

I religiously practiced this breath when I was first introduced to breathwork and experienced the calmest, most present stage in my life during that time. If you are searching for peace of mind and body, please practice this breath.

Dr. Andrew Weil, a well-respected and wise physician is a big proponent of this breath. You can google "Andrew Weil" and "4/7/8 breath" to see what he has to say if you're curious. You can also find instructional videos online for this breath.

Brahmari Breath (Bumble Bee Breath) – This is an ancient breathing practice that works to activate the parasympathetic nervous system and relieve anxiety and depression. I recommend practicing this pranayama anytime you have the time and want to decrease brain chatter and relieve anxiety. It is also very helpful for depressive symptoms.

The following is an excerpt (pg. 77-79) from the book *Shakti Naam Yoga* written by Dr. Joseph Michael Levry:

Posture: Sit in easy pose with a straight spine and a slight Neck Lock.

Focus: Gaze at the third eye, the region between your eyebrows.

Mudra: The index fingers are then placed on the eyelids. The middle fingers are placed on the nose above the nostrils. The ring fingers are placed above the upper lip. The pinkie fingers are placed under the lower lip. Apply light pressure with the thumb and fingers.

Mantra/Breath: OM

Take a few breaths to settle in and notice the state of your mind. Now inhale deeply through your nose and chant an extended OM as you exhale, keeping the mouth and lips closed. It should be a loud high-pitched humming sound, similar to the sound of a bee. Notice how the sound waves gently vibrate your tongue, teeth and sinuses. The sound should be smooth, even and stable. The exhalation should be as long as possible, with concentration on humming sound.

Repeat chanting in this fashion for seven rounds of breath. After the seventh repetition, continue with your normal breathing. Notice the change.

Then repeat again for seven rounds. After the seventh repetition, continue with your normal breathing. Notice the change.

Try to feel the vibration of in your lips, throat, neck and head as well as from the tips of your fingers and toes to your whole brain. Employ your imagination. Imagine that sound is vibrating your entire brain that divine bliss is descending on you and that deep divine wisdom fills your entire being.

Repeat the OM again now for 5 minutes.

Time: *11 minutes total*

Each OM is approximately 20-30 seconds. After 7 repetitions, rest for a moment and notice the change. Then repeat the 7 repetitions and rest noticing the change. Then repeat the sequence a third time for 5 minutes.

Precaution: *If your anxiety is severe and/or you suffer from claustrophobia, you may not enjoy the mudra. You may choose to do the same sound with Gyan mudra instead. Touch your thumb to the index finger and rest them on your knees.*

Comments: *Brahmari is a safe, easy-to learn breathing practice or pranayama, with tremendous therapeutic potential. The cerebral cortex sends impulses via vibrations directly to the hypothalamus, which controls the pituitary or master gland. The word 'Brahmari' originates from the Sanskrit word Brahmar, which means humming bee.*

As the name suggests, a humming sound is created when performing this method of breath control or pranayama. When you make a sound, it literally vibrates from the top of your head down to the tips of your toes, whether you can sense it or not.

Different pitches vibrate at different frequencies. Bass notes and other low-pitched sounds vibrate slowly, whereas high-pitched sounds vibrate quickly, some at thousands of times per second.

Like other pranayamas, the power of Brahmari Pranayama comes partly from its effects on the autonomic nervous system.

Brahmari relieves stress and cerebral tension because it activates the parasympathetic nervous system. It can be a healing process for the person who is in a state of mental tension.

For those who suffer from anxiety or depression, this practice can begin to quiet the mind within a few breaths. The noise of Brahmari's incessant buzzing can drown out the endless mental tape loops that can fuel emotional suffering, at least for a few minutes, making it a useful starting point for those whose minds are "too busy" to meditate. This practice also facilitates easy, trouble-free childbirth when practiced regularly during pregnancy...

Nutritional Psychiatry for Anxiety

The optimal diet for anxiety symptoms would be to avoid or restrict caffeine, alcohol, and refined carbohydrates, to eat regularly planned meals on time, and to control food allergies. If you are lacking nutrition from your diet, the following supplements may be helpful.

- Magnesium: 350 to 500mg per day
- Vitamin D3: 2,000 to 4,000 IU per day (ideally you should measure blood levels and adjust the dose based upon laboratory values)
- Vitamin B6: 25 to 50mg per day
- Folic acid: 800mcg per day
- Vitamin B12: 800mcg per day
- Fish Oils: 1,000 to 3,000mg per day (EPA + DHA)
- Flaxseed Oils: 1tbsp per day

- Grape seed extract: 100 to 300mg per day
- Plant-based antioxidant that provides oxygen radical ab-sorption capacity (ORAC) of 3,000 to 6,000 units or more per day. This can usually be found in popular "super greens" formulas.

Herbs/Plant Medicine

Kava (Piper methysticum) – May be the most underutilized treat-ment that works for anxiety.

Take 45 to 70mg kavalactones three times per day.

Although there have been reports in the past of rare liver toxicity when using kava, most studies recently have shown that it is safe to use when used without any other drugs that may be harmful to the liver.

Ibogaine – Please see Chapter 11 on PTSD for more information on how ibogaine may be helpful for anxiety.

CBD oil – I highly recommend daily CBD oil for any person with mild to severe anxiety. It decreases neuroinflammation and can help with a host of other health problems as well. I personally use CBD oil daily and have heard testimonies from many patients and trusted practitioners who have successfully used it to treat anxiety, depression, and addictions and taper off of psychiatric medications. It seems to help most health conditions but is particularly effective for the treatment of anxiety.

I use Recept CBD oil by Prime My Body because it comes from a clean, organic, trusted source, is third-party tested, more bioavail-able than competitors, more rapidly absorbed, and it works. I have personally met many of the people involved in this company, looked them in the eyes, and found them to be people of high integrity and pure intentions. Their product reflects the people. Thus, I have signed up to represent them and distribute the product, which I be-lieve will help heal the world. Marijuana is a plant that has evolved with human beings and has great potential to help people. The CBD portion of the plant has tremendous healing capacity, for most, if not all, medical conditions.

Medical Marijuana – I like to refer to cannabis as Santa Maria. She is a sacred plant. For those who feel called to work with her, I encourage you to consider why and to set a conscious intention prior to use. She has consciousness and will honor your intention. She can open energetic portals to many dimensions, and it is important to feel like you are in a safe space, supported, and in an environment where you can feel safe to explore, forgive, heal, and create.

Those who work with marijuana unintentionally tend to go through a series of stages that mimic aspects of other relationships. From my experience and observation, these can include: silliness, laughter, joy, friendship, ecstasy, dependence, and finally, addiction. Loneliness, anger/agitation, avoidance, paranoia, and panic can then follow. Through these stages, the experiencer can learn a lot about herself, the world, and the truth.

Santa Maria wants to evolve with humans and help them. She can help with sleep, anxiety, pain, and inflammation, but like any plant, if abused, she can turn from being your ally or friend to being your master. Therefore, it is important to work with her with conscious intention and in the right set and setting. I would also highly recommend working with a trusted friend/herbalist who has your best interests in mind and can give you unbiased, truthful, educational, and experiential support when needed. Or, simply do your own research!

Generally speaking, for anxiety, find a safe, calm, peaceful space and ingest a low dose of an Indica strain while listening to peaceful music, practicing the 4/7/8 breath, or listening to a guided meditation.

For sleep, it may be useful to use a low-dose Indica 30 minutes before bed. Use in conjunction with abdominal breathing and 528hz-frequency, low-volume music or play subconscious mind reprogramming affirmations in the background.

As one grows their consciousness, they may become more sensitive to the portals that the plant is opening. For sensitive beings, it might be important to be in a safe setting with only trusted souls. However, please realize every soul is unique. There are some outgoing extroverts who have harmonized so much with the plant that they can be in any setting and feel comfortable and confident. Some call Santa Maria the "Tree of Life," as it has tremendous potential to help with a host of dis-eases (especially the non-psychoactive part of the plant is referred to as hemp). However, working with her is a calling whether one is aware of it or not.

If it were not for Santa Maria, I may not be alive today. She helped me transition off of alcohol, into a calmer, healthier lifestyle, and for that I am eternally grateful to her. These days, I rarely work with her, as she has become a part of my being. If I do choose to work with her, I do so ceremonially with the intention to enhance creativity and connect with Mother Nature or to be shown a more loving perspective about a situation I find myself in. Santa Maria is here to help. Approach her with humility, teachability, and a pure intention, and she can help you.

Essential Oils – Human consciousness is just starting to reawaken to the potential of what is possible with essential oils. Plants have been around longer than humans. All day and night, they are absorbing the energy of the sun, moon, water, wind, and earth. When we work with them, we work with their essences. The essences of these plants contain wisdom and healing potential that humans are just starting to learn about. Essential oils are mentioned time and time again in the Bible. For example, hyssop is mentioned numerous times and is associated with purification and forgiveness. The Israelites, when marking their doorposts with lambs' blood for the Angel of Death to pass over them, were instructed to use paintbrushes made of hyssop. King David exclaims in Psalm 51:7, "Cleanse me with hyssop and I will be clean..." Mary, so overwhelmed with love for Jesus, bought expensive essential oils, including spikenard and, in the middle of a gathering, got down on her knees and washed Jesus' feet and was severely criticized for it. Mary was experienced with essential oils and found that they contained tremendous healing potential.

For anxiety, there are many essential oils that can prove helpful. These include valerian, lavender, jasmine, holy basil, chamomile, and vetiver, among others. I would recommend doing your own research. As you ingest or sniff the oil as directed, the essence of the plant will infuse into your bloodstream and spread to areas of the brain, including the limbic system, and bring a soothing, calming influence. Essential oils have the potential to help with every disease and can open someone up to a whole new world/dimension of healing. From my own research, the company I most trust is Wisdom of the Earth.

CHAPTER 7:
PSYCHOSIS

A. A Conscious Paradigm of Psychosis

Psychosis is when conscious and subconscious belief systems produce distorted thoughts, which become low-vibration energy frequencies and patterns, which then attract the same frequency energy and entities, leading to classic symptoms such as paranoia, delusions, or hallucinations.

Psychosis may be as simple as a child who was brought up to always care about what other people think to the point where they are punished anytime they did anything that upset anyone. These children are usually very emotionally sensitive and adopt a belief system in which they are very concerned with what others think, to the point where it comes even before their own needs. Then, as an adult, this sensitive soul is sitting next to businessman in a rush on a train in Europe. The man gives her/him an angry look because she/he has placed a bag next to the man, who feels the bag is invading his space. The man continues to give the person angry energy throughout the duration of the long train trip. The sensitive soul first starts to have thoughts like *Is this person mad at me?* These thoughts subconsciously become *What did I do wrong?* Then, *What's wrong with me?* This leads to the experiencer feeling the low-vibration frequencies of guilt and paranoia. Because the person is so sensitive, even after the train ride, they are still thinking about the event, stuck in the energy of the past, and still vibrating the low-frequency emotions. After they have been thinking about the event for one day, it becomes part of their mood. If they are still thinking about the event 30 days later, it becomes etched into their personality. If they are still thinking about the event one year later, it becomes a part of their character. This leads to being in a low-frequency emotional state for chronic period of time, which then by the law of attraction starts leading to isolation, fear, guilt, shame, and dis-ease. Because the experiencer is so sensitive and doesn't want to "hurt" other people, they start to isolate, which is the worst thing a person can do for their health. This can then lead to the person going to see a psychiatrist, who then places them on antipsychotics, which shut down the energy center of the frontal lobe, making it nearly impossible for the person to ever regain their awareness to the point of complete recovery. Awareness is the first step of change, and when the frontal lobe is shut down, it makes it very difficult to become aware of the root problem. Now they are stuck in the cycle of westernized mental health treatment and put on medications that can cause temporary and permanent side effects.

This is not to downplay the fact that many people are more prone to psychosis than others. Many have a genetic lineage and karmic debt that predisposes them to be emotionally sensitive and vulnerable to what modern society calls "psychosis." Many people who have "psychosis" have been brought up in families that subconsciously have nurtured an environment that predisposes a person to the symptoms exhibited by the disorder. This is often seen in people brought up in strictly religious families with a lot of rules and with the idea ingrained into them that there is a God "upstairs" who watches everything they do, punishes those who are "bad," and rewards those who are "good." They began to see their condition as "bad" and get lost into the endless sea of thoughts that come with that belief system. They start to believe they are "sinners" and get lost in the emotions of guilt, shame, and fear, which attract the same energies from the Universe. Shamanistic cultures label these energies as entities, while modern science uses the term psyche or neurosis. Whatever label is used, one view is that these entities or neurosis are simply a collection of all of the "fears" that have been programmed and conditioned into the mind. Some spiritually minded people would say that they are living in the "realm of hungry ghosts." This simply means that there are energies or entities that are attracted to certain frequencies and like to attach to those human beings who are vulnerable and open to the energies they want to latch on to. This can often times lead to what many term auditory and visual hallucinations, which we loosely categorize into the word "schizophrenia."

Psychosis can also be precipitated by severe trauma, which is stored in the body in the organs, tissues, and cells. After a severe traumatic event, the experiencer will often times disassociate because they no longer feel safe in their body. They are often times subconsciously afraid that they will experience the trauma again, and their mind becomes stuck in the past, therefore causing fear of the future, while never being present in their bodies. This then leads to a cycle of low-vibration emotions, which precipitate isolation and psychosis. Human beings were meant to live with other humans in a tribe. When isolated, many animals will become "psychotic." Then the system, which now has labeled "psychosis" as a disease, starts to view the person as "unfit" to live in society, which leads the person to further isolation and dis-ease.

It is interesting to see that many of these patients then will adopt a lifestyle of isolation and inactivity, which further contributes to the low-frequency vibrations they are emitting. The psychiatric medications they are placed on also contribute to the low-vibration frequencies by effectively shutting down certain energy centers, or chakras, within the body.

Often times, psychosis is induced by "drug" use or a kundalini awakening. Many times, a patient will take a substance, such as marijuana, LSD, cocaine, amphetamines, or other psychedelics, such as ayahuasca or psilocybin, which will precipitate a healing crisis. Often times these experiences are a highly "spiritual" and very real for the person going through it. During this experience, there is a rise in consciousness, which leads to new neural synapses and connections in the brain as well as bodily biochemical changes. From an energetic perspective, what is usually happening is that the chakras or energy centers to the upper world are open, but the experiencer does not have the ability to ground the information into a coherent structure or foundation; this is particularly true in cases where the experiencer does not have a support system or mentor. The lower chakras are usually unable to integrate the scrambled energy/information during the experience, and the person is quickly labeled as psychotic by a psychiatrist, if taken to one by friends/family, and placed into the endless cycle of westernized psychiatry. The person will be put on medications that disrupt his biochemistry and numb the new neural connections so that the symptoms temporarily improve. However, once Western medicine is involved, it is nearly impossible to treat the root cause of what is actually happening.

Often times, "schizophrenics" are actually emotionally sensitive people experiencing an ungrounded spiritual experience that does not makes "sense" to the rest of society. Because the experiencer has experienced what they have, they know it to be true for themselves while all other members of society will think the person is "crazy." When the child or adult is taken to an inpatient psychiatric hospital, which happens in many cases, this further depletes the trust the experiencer had with whomever it is that took them to the hospital, which is usually another family member. It often times will take time and loving, honest communication to heal the trust that has been damaged.

In some countries that are more in tune with nature, when a young adult from the ages of 16 to 24 starts to experience what we describe in Western culture as psychosis, they actually view the person as someone who has a special connection with the unseen world. In these cultures, a shaman or mentor takes the youth under their wing and guides them through the process because they themselves remember when they first started having their symptoms of hallucinations or "psychosis."

After the shaman embraces the youth, the community starts to see the youth as "special." This does not mean the youth will have an easy road ahead; in fact, the contrary. The young adult will be taught how to navigate the unseen world and be given tools to help them stay grounded in themselves throughout the upcoming process of spiritual growth. With a loving community, a proper mentor, and the right tools, the youth emerges as an adult with a gift of connecting with the unseen world and can become the local town shaman. These shamans, because they have conquered their own "demons," are able to help others navigate the process of spiritual growth. They have also learned, through their own journey, the tools, herbs, plants, and consciousness required to heal or integrate many "conditions."

Please note that if Jesus or many "saints" of the past were to be born today into a typical Western family, many of them would likely be labeled as schizophrenic and placed on psychiatric medications. Jesus was quoted as saying He was the "Son of God." These saints were either saints and were telling the truth or were crazy schizophrenics. There is a thin line that separates a saint from a psychotic person. Holy men of the past have had a framework for their belief system, a community that believed in them, and had grounded the energy of the unseen world into their physical bodies. Many people today who have been labeled as schizophrenic are spiritually minded people who have had experiences with the unseen world but do not have a framework for their belief system or experience and are unable to ground the erratic energy of their minds into the present moment and their lower energy centers. They also do have mentors or loving communities that embrace their experiences or help them ground the energy into the physical world.

Western medicine does not teach anything about intuition, the sixth sense. It teaches nothing about the astral world. It teaches nothing about how energy is everything. It teaches nothing about the intelligence of the heart. It teaches nothing about breathwork or meditation. It teaches nothing about the interconnectedness of all of nature. Therefore, Western medicine can only approach schizophrenia from a framework of what makes sense in the analytical/mental mind. Many symptoms of schizophrenia, however, cannot be adequately understood or treated by simply focusing on the limited perspective of westernized, analytical, linear-minded science. Many symptoms of schizophrenia can be attributed to matters of the heart and the astral world. It is the unseen world that controls or manifests into the seen world. What we see is less than 10% of reality. What we do not see is usually where the symptoms have started. Therefore, to effectively treat symptoms one must know where to treat the root cause of the symptoms, which is the unseen world.

Kundalini awakenings can often be mislabeled as psychosis by modern Western psychiatrists. Kundalini is a mysterious, mystical, and pure energy, which mystics know reside in each person at the base of the spine. This energy will often be "awakened" when the person is ready or purposefully attempts to awaken this energy. Although each experience is different, the person will usually go through a series of mystical and sometimes confusing experiences of awakening. This is usually accompanied by a heightened sense of awareness to many synchronicities and many unexplainable experiences. One who is experiencing a kundalini awakening often times will feel like they are going "crazy." If they do not have a proper support system, or framework for understanding what is happening to them, they will often go to see a psychiatrist who will immediately label them as psychotic, perhaps even giving them the label of schizophrenia and placing them on mind-numbing toxic medications. The spiritual awakening will effectively be numbed; therefore, the experiencer will never be able to fully process the awakening.

We are entering an age where the veil between science and spirituality will become thinner. Even scientists will start to realize that science will slowly start to catch up to the science of energy also termed spirituality. To be comfortable in this time of rapid change, we will need to move from our analytical mind to our heart space.

B. Westernized Psychiatry and Psychosis

Modernized Western medicine views psychosis strictly from a checklist of symptoms. This checklist of symptoms continues to be edited as society changes and is based upon the *DSM*. The diagnostic criteria for schizophrenia have changed significantly from the fourth to the fifth edition of the *DSM*, and these changes are outlined in the fifth edition. I encourage you to take a look at the symptoms and categorization of the disorder online.

To be honest, most psychiatrists aren't able to keep up with the constantly changing checklist of symptoms, qualifiers, and terminology. You could go to five different psychiatrists and come home with five different diagnoses. There is little consistency or precision in the current Western model of establishing psychiatric diagnoses. This is important because once you've been labeled by a psychiatrist with a disorder, not only can it effect your entire medical record but also your entire mental attitude and spirit. Once one believes they have a diagnosis, and that there is a chemical imbalance, they start to produce proteins and hormones that correspond to this belief. In today's Western model, most psychiatrists don't have sufficient time to spend with their clients. Thus, they are pressured and forced to write down a psychiatric diagnosis in haste, without thinking twice about how the diagnosis will impact the rest of the patient's life. In insurance-based models, psychiatrists have to write down a diagnosis, even if there is none, in order to be paid. Then the psychiatrist most often places the patient on a medication, which will require regular follow-up visits while never curing the condition. Then the patient will become numb in the frontal lobe, which will effectively eliminate the judgement necessary to navigate the condition. Then the body will adjust, and the medication will cease to effectively numb the symptoms. The patient will then have a "psychotic break" and be placed into a psychiatric hospital and administered different medications or very high dosages of antipsychotics, which will then effectively shut down all energy centers, leaving the "patient" in a zombie state.

As you can see, the criteria for psychosis is in a process of constant flux and change based upon a history of often-unreliable research articles and papers and other psychiatrists' opinions and votes. Though I love psychiatrists, and most have good intentions, I can tell you firsthand that we are a weird bunch with many different opinions. If you want to experience a frustrating meeting, try sitting in a circle of 20 different psychiatrists trying to decide on what criteria to include as psychotic—never mind trying to decide what food to order for the Christmas celebration event. The point being that if I were a loving parent, I would not be content with the current way the system diagnoses, labels, and treats "psychosis." It is a system that does not train its doctors to understand the energetics behind "psychosis" and then trains them to treat the symptoms with life-altering drugs that don't actually treat the cause and often times don't even effectively band-aid the symptoms. Not to mention the emotional trauma caused by the label "schizophrenic" and the numerous inpatient hospitalizations, which can sometimes be similar to visits to jail. Also, to get out of the hospitals, it is often required that you take medications. Once again, I would like to reiterate that every single case and person is different. Sometimes "psychosis" can be a kundalini or spiritual awakening. Most often it is because the use of substances led to an altered state of thought that does not have a framework or proper grounding. This means that the person has experienced a spiritual/consciousness expanding event in their higher energy centers or chakras but has no way of grounding the experience into their lower energy centers/chakras. Therefore, they will be unable to even talk about it logically, nonetheless explain it to a psychiatrist. Thus, most of these people will be labeled as psychotic and placed on medications. Often in inpatient hospitals those labeled as psychotic have experienced a deep trauma or loss or have been using illicit substances to cover up trauma or pain. Whatever the root cause, the person is led to isolation and consistent low-vibration emotions, which attract the same energies and/or entities to it. This leads to a lifetime of suffering and a cycle of medications, hospitalizations, and dis-ease.

C. Westernized Treatment of Psychosis

Currently, the standard of care for treatment of psychosis is with "antipsychotics." This includes medications such as Risperdal, Zyprexa, Geodon, Abilify, haloperidol, etc. The proposed theory is that psychosis is caused by an elevation of dopamine levels, but there isn't actually any scientific proof for this. Thus, the drugs all at some level are supposed to block the action of dopamine, which does seem to band-aid symptoms and dull the patient temporarily and quickly. However, dopamine has several different receptor sub-types, thus leading to many side effects, such as muscle spasms, weight gain, sluggishness, and feeling like a "zombie." Long term, these medications can lead to diabetes, obesity, permanent movement disorders, and a permanent alteration of the brain. Most people placed on these medications will not be able to effectively hold a job.

On an energetic level, these medications are likely shutting down the energies of the frontal lobe as well as numerous other energy centers in the body and creating a numbing chemical imbalance.

It will likely be said 50 years from now that psychiatrists were "chemically lobotomizing" their patients with mind-numbing drugs and calling it a treatment. Most are already subconsciously aware of this but are too entrained into the system to do anything about it.

D. Natural Treatment Approaches Towards Psychosis

Breathwork

Sodarchan Chakra Kriya – This practice uses prana to cleanse mental garbage out of the subconscious mind and purify it. It is a powerful exercise for all who suffer from neurosis or psychosis and is highly recommended. Please realize that all treatments for psychosis that work from the outside in will not effectively cure the disease. This exercise stimulates the pressure from within, and it works. It should NOT BE practiced if someone is in an acute state of psychosis. This is for the person who may have been diagnosed with psychosis in the past, however is currently stable, grounded, and has proper community support. This is a powerful practice that could lead to mystical experiences and without the proper grounding, could lead someone to feel unstable. Only practice this when you feel able to stay grounded.

For detailed instructions, please see the book by Dr. Joseph Michael Levry, entitled, *Lifting the Veil*, pg. 136-137. The following is a copy of the meditation found in the book. **If you do this exercise consistently, it will clear the subconscious mind of garbage, thus alleviating symptoms of psychosis, neurosis, anxiety, and depression!** This breath is a gift to humanity. This kriya will teach you breath control, which will lead to better control of the mind and your life.

Posture: *Sit with spine straight (legs crossed or in a chair with feet flat on floor). Eyes focused on tip of nose or closed if preferred.*

Hand Position and Breath:

1. Block off the right nostril with the right thumb. Inhale slowly and deeply through the left nostril and hold the breath. Mentally chant WAHE GURU 16 times, while pumping the navel point 3 times with each repetition (pump once on WAA, once on HEY, and once on GURU), for a total of 48 pumps. WA is infinity; HE is the presence of the finite in infinity; GU is darkness; and RU is light. Together WAHE GURU means Indescribable Wisdom.

2. Unblock the right nostril and use the right index or pinkie finger to block the left nostril. Exhale slowly and deeply through the right nostril. Continue, inhaling left nostril, exhaling right.

To end the meditation, inhale and hold 5-10 seconds. Exhale. Then stretch and shake the body for about 1 minute to circulate the energy.

Time: *Suggested length for this meditation is 31 or 62 minutes a day. The ideal is to start at 31 minutes, but you can begin with 11 minutes, and then build up to 31, then 40, and eventually 62.*

Comments: *This meditation can be used for almost any condition with success. It will create a potent platform for growth and healing* as well as the perfect conditions for releasing deeply rooted patterns. Sodarchan Chakra Kriya can be done for up to 62 minutes per day. In some cases, it can be gradually increased up to 2 ½ hours a day, which is 1/10th of the day. It will give you Nao nidhi, atara sidhi, which are the 9 precious virtues and 18 esoteric powers. In theses 27 total virtues of the world lies the entire universe. Sodarchan Chakra Kriya can be traced back to the sacred text, Siri Guru Granth Sahib.

Nutritional Therapy for Schizophrenia

Abram Hoffer was one of the pioneers who researched diet and nutritional supplements for schizophrenia. Although westernized psychiatry tends to believe that a diagnosis of schizophrenia has no cure, or hope for remission, according to Hoffer's research, this was not true. He reported that the natural recovery of "schizophrenics" is 50% if the patient is provided with shelter, good food, and attention to personal dignity and respect. He also stated that with nutritional therapy is added, 90% of acute schizophrenics (those who have been sick less than two years or have had several remissions and relapses) recover within two years. 65-75% of chronic schizophrenics treated with nutritional therapy were much improved or well within 10 years! Nutritional therapy can also help the patient lower their antipsychotic medications to low, non-toxic doses. Please note that it takes at least two months of nutritional therapy for the supplementation to start working.

In Hoffer's research, he found that vitamin B3 (niacinamide or niacin), vitamin C, and vitamin B6 were essential ingredients. Dietary recommendations were to **eliminate refined sugar** and any allergenic foods from the diet, which were wheat, dairy products, and corn.

Vitamin B3 – is the **most important nutrient for treating schizophrenia**, which has been validated by several studies.

Take 1,000mg three times per day. Monitor periodically for hepatotoxicity. Specifically, monitor serum aminotransferase levels. After 30 years of study, Hoffer hypothesized that 1 in 2,000 patients may develop hepatitis from vitamin B3.

Please note that for chronic schizophrenia, Hoffer recommended this dose of vitamin B3, for at least two years before symptomatic improvement can be seen. It is also recommended that the dose of antipsychotics be slowly tapered with a physician as vitamin B3 is introduced.

Vitamin C – Take 500-6,000mg/day.

Vitamin B6 – Take 75-3,000mg/day. Any patient receiving more than 200mg/day should be monitored for the development of sensory neuropathy.

Magnesium – Take 300-600mg/day.

Omega-3 Fatty Acids – Take 3-10g/day of fish oil or 1-3 g/day of EPA.

Zinc – Take 15-30mg/day and manganese (10-20mg/day) in selected cases.

N-Acetylcysteine – Take 1g twice a day for negative symptoms of schizophrenia. (Negative symptoms include blunting of affect, poverty of speech and thought, apathy, anhedonia, reduced social drive, loss of motivation, lack of social interest, and inattention to social or cognitive input).

DHEA –For schizophrenic patients whose serum DHEA-sulfate concentration is below or in the bottom 10-20% of the normal range, take 10-50mg/day for men and 5-25mg/day for women.

Chapter 8:
Alzheimer's Dementia

A. A New Paradigm of Alzheimer's

Alzheimer's disease is caused by inflammation, of which sources can include diet, toxins, the environment, and toxic thoughts/energy. To reverse Alzheimer's, treat the cause(s) of inflammation. When the brain is provided with a neuro-permissive environment, it will heal itself.

Dementia can be loosely defined as a cognitive decline usually accompanied by memory loss and a decline in mental capacity. Currently in Western medicine, dementia is subclassed into vascular dementia, frontotemporal dementia, Lewy body dementia, and Alzheimer's dementia. Although all subtypes can be defined in their own medical jargon, for the purposes of this book we will lump all subclasses into one category of dementia, knowing that each subtype stems from a cause of either inflammation, toxins, lack of nutrients, or all three. Prior to diagnosis by a neurologist, the experiencer can enter the phases of subjective cognitive impairment (SCI) and/or Mild Cognitive Impairment (MCI). SCI means that despite normal testing, the individual subjectively feels cognitive decline, which will then usually progress into MCI. MCI means neuropsychological testing will reveal mild cognitive decline despite maintaining an ability to function.

Medical science has led many people to believe that cognitive decline is irreversible. This is absolutely not true. For many decades, the prevalent view in Western medicine is that there is no cure or effective treatment for Alzheimer's dementia. This has led to a sense of hopelessness and helplessness for those who were previously diagnosed. As more research comes forth, we are starting to

105

realize that there is hope and that Alzheimer's dementia is actually treatable and sometimes even reversible. The general medical community is starting to realize that Alzheimer's is a chronic onset condition, which develops from a chronic buildup of inflammation and toxic substances along with a decline and shortage of supportive nutrients and hormones. So, simply identifying the chronic causes of inflammation and toxins and effectively removing them are a great place to start in the treatment process. This alone can sometimes lead to complete prevention and/or reversal of the condition. Dale Bresden introduces revolutionary ideas and treatment protocols in his book titled *The End of Alzheimer's: The First Program to Prevent and Reverse Cognitive Decline.*

Despite the billions of dollars put into Alzheimer's research for a cure, the medical community has yet to come up with one treatment that is effective. Therefore, when anyone receives a diagnosis of Alzheimer's disease, they believe that they are destined for a long, cruel journey into forgetfulness, torture, depending on others for help, and the victimhood of hopeless despair. The few medications that are on the market hardly even decrease the symptoms of Alzheimer's never mind stop the course of the disease. And when someone loses hope, they lose their purpose and will to live. When someone loses their purpose to live, the soul or Spirit starts its process of preparing to leave the body.

For many years, the prevailing hypothesis of Western scientists was that sticky synapse-destroying plaques called amyloid beta accumulate in the brain, destroying the brain's ability to communicate. However, all the treatments aimed at destroying these plaques didn't work. The assumption in Western medicine that Alzheimer's is a single disease and can be treated as such ignores the obvious fact of the interconnectedness of All that is. The brain is connected to the gut via the vagus nerve, and to the rest of the body, and all affects all. Trying to simply destroy one protein is not going to solve Alzheimer's. The two most popular medications on the market, Aricept and Nameda, adhere to this costly assumption. They inhibit the enzyme cholinesterase from destroying acetylcholine, a neurotransmitter responsible for how we think, feel, and move. In my clinical practice working with Alzheimer's patients for over a year, I found that these medications seldom work. They hardly reduce symptoms and never cure the actual cause of the disease. At best, they can sometimes slow down the progression of the disease while likely causing other side effects downstream. Bottom line is that there is no medication on the market that actually deals with the root cause.

It is my belief, however, that not only can the disease be prevented, but the cognitive decline, if caught early enough, can be reversed. The brain has neuroplasticity, which means neurons can regenerate if the cause of the inflammation and the toxins are removed and replaced with life-rejuvenating elements and energy. Previous research has suggested that those who are gene carriers of the Apolipoprotein E gene (commonly called ApoE4) are at greater risk of Alzheimer's. We now have the technology for everyone to get gene tested, and if those tested are found to be carriers of the ApoE4 gene, they can begin steps to prevent cognitive decline and maintain healthy brains despite their carrier status.

The research seems to suggest that those who are carriers of ApoE4 are more susceptible to the disease. Amyloid Precursor Protein (APP) is what becomes the amyloid plaques. APP can be cut in two ways, which will result in two molecules that prevent Alzheimer's, or cut into four, which would support the progression of the disease. It is believed that ApoE4 encourages the retention of the harmful amyloid beta and attaches to DNA, encouraging certain gene expressions. Many have started to categorize Alzheimer's into different categories depending on the ApoE4 variants. Dresden, in his book, describes type 1 as primarily inflammatory while carrying the ApoE4 gene expression. The chances of having atrophic or subtype II is also increased by carriers of ApoE4. This subtype is primarily due to an insufficiency of vital nutrients and exposure to poisonous substances. Type 3 is more common in people with ApoE3 rather than ApoE4, and therefore is not hereditary. This subtype usually manifests after periods of extreme stress and often occurs as early as one's late 40s. Symptoms begin with loss of cognitive abilities. Some characteristics of this type include brain damage, high levels of toxins in the blood, too much copper, and insufficient zinc. Dresden's treatment changes based on the primary type of dementia the sufferer is experiencing, which is determined through testing.

It is important to come to the realization that Alzheimer's is not a result of the brain doing something wrong but a result of the brain adjusting and trying to protect itself from years of toxins and inflammation. It is a result of the brain trying to protect itself and repair itself or, in other words, the result of the brain's normal functioning gone bad.

It is important to realize that a person's lifestyle patterns are largely what contribute to the development of Alzheimer's. This not only includes the person's choice of diet, relationships, and environment they choose to surround themselves in but also the quality of their belief system, thoughts, and emotions. Eating sugary foods and insufficient sleep can lead to inflammation. The chronic stress that our thoughts and emotions put on our body also contribute to chronic inflammation. The truth is that there are likely over 40 or more contributing factors for each individual. The key is to identify the main causes and eliminate and treat them as early as possible.

The standard American diet includes foods that contain gluten, dairy, and grains, which can often lead to gut inflammation. Infections, viruses, and pathogens can also lead to chronic inflammation. For some, maintaining a gluten-free diet can be a good place to start. Another good place to start is by eliminating sugar from the diet. Sugar can cause short-term and chronic inflammation and is the number one addiction on the planet currently. High levels of sugar in the body over a long period of time can lead to insulin resistance, which also can increase the chances of dementia. Another way to fortify brain health is by living an intellectually engaging life, which will decrease the negative effects of amyloid invasion. Also, supplying the brain with nutrients, hormones, and trophic factors that it needs to regenerate and grow is a protective action. Another way of preventing and reversing dementia is by getting rid of the toxins that cause it. This can include copper, mycotoxins, molds, etc. Amyloid can be released when toxic substances invade the body.

B. Current Scientific Paradigm of Alzheimer's Dementia

The first step in treatment of Alzheimer's is to identify which of the threats are contributing to the condition: inflammation, toxins, and/or a lack of nutrients, hormones, and brain-supporting materials. Laboratory tests can help test for the presence of ApoE gene as well as for inflammatory markers, infections, homocysteine, insulin resistance, hormone levels, toxic metals exposure, immune system testing, presence of bacteria, etc. Laboratory tests, however, can be unaffordable for the general public. Therefore, simply adjusting one's lifestyle to adhere to the NEWSTART™ regimen would be a great place to start.

For those who can afford laboratory testing, the following labs may be helpful in identifying the treatable causes of dementia.

Homocysteine is an amino acid, and increased levels are indicative of either inflammation or insufficient hormones and nutrients. It is often contained in foods like beef, eggs, beans, nuts, dairy, shellfish, or soy. Vitamins B6, B12, and folate (B9) are all needed to maintain low homocysteine. It would be ideal to check these levels.

Excess sugars in the body leads to high glucose and insulin resistance, which leads to inflammation and insufficient brain nutrition. Ideal fasting insulin levels would be 4.5 or below while glucose should be 90 or lower. Eliminating sugars, such as candy and soda, and starchy foods, such as white bread, white rice and white potatoes, is a good place to start.

Other inflammatory markers include C-reactive protein, albumin-globulin ratio, omega-6/omega-3 ratio, and increased levels of cytokines IL-6 and TNF alpha.

Vitamin D3 is essential for the formation and health of brain synapses. A decreased level of vitamin D3 can be indicative of cognitive degeneration.

Shortage of hormones, such as estrogen, progesterone, thyroid, testosterone, cortisol, pregnenolone, and dehydroepiandrosterone (DHEA), can also signal a decline in cognitive ability.

Elevated copper along with insufficient zinc is also an indication of decreased cognitive function. When magnesium levels are low, it interferes with ideal brain functioning. Selenium works with glutathione to rid the body of molecules that can cause cognitive decline. It would be good to check selenium and glutathione levels. Heavy metals, such as mercury, lead, arsenic, and cadmium, can also cause cognitive impairment. These will show up on a heavy metal screen. Sleep apnea can lead to cognitive decline as well, and one may consider an apnea-hypopnea index evaluation. Also, check your cholesterol, as low levels can put people at a higher risk of cognitive impairment. Vitamin E protects the cell membranes, and ideal levels can be protective over cognitive decline. Thiamine, also known as Vitamin B1, improves memory formation.

Recently many have been writing about "leaky gut" or gastrointestinal permeability. Leaky gut is usually caused by inflammatory foods and makes one more vulnerable to systemic inflammation and dementia. Gluten sensitivity tests may be in alignment for those who feel sensitivity to wheat-based foods. A Cyrex Array test can test for blood-brain barrier permeability and can also test for whether you are producing autoantibodies against yourself. Testing for toxins, such as molds and mycotoxins, can be helpful in narrowing down the cause of the inflammation. Please also note that for ideal cognitive function, a body mass index between 18-25 is considered ideal. However, everybody is different, and maintaining a positive mindset and low-stress environment is even more important than body mass.

Those who want to test for memory status and cognitive decline can see a neuropsychologist who can do a series of tests, which will likely include a Montreal Cognitive Assessment test (MOCA). A normal MOCA is a score between 26-30. **One can also obtain this testing online and have a trusted loved one administer it.**

Brain imaging may help reveal any problematic areas in the brain as well. However, the most important aspect of assessment is a thorough personal history regarding one's lifestyle and environment. For most, it is not necessary to get all of the laboratory tests. Simple changes in lifestyle and working with a trusted health care expert would be a good starting point.

It is important to realize that thoughts, words, and actions can also be causes of stress and inflammation. Some people may make all the right dietary changes, take all the right supplements, and do yoga every day but still wind up with dementia. This is because one's thoughts, words, and actions are medicine on an even deeper level than one could ever imagine. Therefore, it is important for the patient showing cognitive decline to be placed in a low-stress environment that is conducive to positive thoughts, words, and actions.

C. Current Westernized Paradigm and Treatment of Alzheimer's

There must be a shift from a 20th century, monotherapy approach to dementia to a more natural, holistic, multi-faceted approach. This means that instead of trying to find one cause of dementia, one must start with the knowing that it is a multi-faceted, chronic condition, which occurs from a toxic lifestyle and inner and outer environment. It is unlikely that Western medicine will adopt this view for several reasons, including that there is no "money" in prevention or lifestyle medicine. Also, if the patients were cured, then there would be no need for medicine. However, the goal of all medicine should be to cure the patient so that they do not need a doctor or have the tools to effectively manage their condition.

As previously mentioned, the main drugs on the market for Alzheimer's, Namenda and Aricept, do not cure the condition and from my clinical practice and experience, hardly make any difference in the symptoms of dementia. If I had a beloved grandmother who was starting to show cognitive decline, I would sit down with her and take a thorough inventory of her diet, lifestyle and environment. I would use the acronym NEWSTART™ and incorporate ideal diet, exercise, hydration, sunshine, nature, fresh air, sleep, and meditation into her lifestyle. I would find her a loving community where she could exercise her mind and find interest in daily activities. I would make her a playlist of her favorite songs and provide her with daily music therapy. If I suspected toxins were contributing to her condition, I would find a trusted physician and get laboratory tests done. Most importantly, I would maintain a mindset that dementia is reversible. In my loved one's presence, I would maintain an attitude that she is perfect and whole the way she is. This attitude alone would have an impact on her health. Remember, as soon as someone starts to believe there is something wrong with them, they start to feel that way and code for proteins and hormones that are in alignment with that belief system. Most of all, it is important to maintain a sense of hope and peace because where there is hope, there is life.

D. Natural Treatment Approaches for Dementia

Kirtan Kriya

For those with mild cognitive impairment who are still able to meditate, kirtan kriya has been proven scientifically to increase blood flow to the brain and has the ability to decrease symptoms and sometimes even reverse neuroinflammation, thus reversing the symptoms of dementia.

A study in the *Journal of Alzheimer's Disease* showed that 12 minutes a day of kirtan kriya for 12 weeks produced the following results, which were sustained at six months: improved cerebral blood flow (helps you think better); improved blood flow to the posterior cingulated gyrus (improves memory retrieval); increased activity in the frontal lobe (sharpens attention, concentration, and focus); replenished vital neurotransmitters and brain chemicals, such as acetylcholine, norepinephrine, and dopamine (help the brain function more smoothly); increased energy levels, improved sleep, and reduced stress (lowers cortisol levels); and improved both long-term psychological health and spiritual wellbeing (Innes, Selfe, Khalsa, & Kandati, 2016).

Simply put, kirtan kriya works. In fact, I will be as bold as to say that the chanting of ancient mantras for emotional, mental, and physical health is one of the greatest ancient secrets. I can give you many reasons as to how it works on a physical level, such as stimulating certain meridian points. On a mental level, mantras are the quickest way to quiet the non-stop chatter/"monkey"/analytical mind. On an energetic level, it is a mystery. All we know that certain holy men of the past would disappear for several days and come back with mantras. It is a great mystery, but I believe and know from experience that the chanting of these ancient mantras heals the body on all levels—spiritually, mentally, and physically. But please, don't believe me. Try it. Ignorance is rejecting something before investigating or trying it. Please don't be ignorant before you even try it. See for yourself if it works. Try the kirtan kriya 11 minutes a day for 30 days consistently and see what happens.

Supplements and Diet

Treatment should be aimed at treating as many of the causes at the root as possible.

This may include a combination of vitamin B6, B12, and folate for elevated homocysteine levels, as well as reducing foods containing methionine.

For insulin resistance, combining the right diet with exercise and adequate sleep can help. **The ideal anti-Alzheimer's diet is called Ketoflex 12/3**. It is aimed at promoting ketosis and helping leaky gut syndrome. It involves a combination of low carbohydrates, exercise, intermittent fasting, MCT oil, and non-starchy vegetables. It is also essential to optimize sleep to get as close to eight hours of sleep as possible without using pills. **Reducing stress is a key component of treating dementia.** Reducing caffeine and alcohol can also help. Having regular exercise contributes to improvement of cognitive ability. Sometimes a combination of supplements, which are anti-inflammatory, can be of help if the person is not getting enough in their regular diet.

Healing the gut by eliminating inflammatory foods, drinking bone soups, and **minimizing sugars/carbohydrates** can be helpful. Probiotics and prebiotics can also help absorb the nutrients from the food. Working with a physician to optimize and regulate hormone levels can be helpful. Eliminating toxins such as mercury by taking zinc can also be helpful as well as a heavy metal detox carried out with a physician.

For those who are interested in more treatment options, Dr. Bredesen has developed a treatment protocol titled Re-Code, and I highly recommend you take a look at his methods as an option for the treatment of dementia. For more information, check out his website at: https://www.ahnphealth.com/dr-bredesen.html

Music Therapy

In my clinical experience of working at skilled nursing facilities and inpatient geriatric units, it was quite clear that though dementia patients may forget their family member's names, they will never forget music. More and more scientific evidence is emerging that dementia patients store the memory of music in parts of the brain and in their cellular memory, which is not affected by dementia. Sound is the medicine of the future, and in dementia patients, time will tell how powerful sound can be. It will often times help patients feel happy, move them to dance, and help them to remember and reexperience the joyful times in their lives. On a cellular level, it will help them code for proteins and hormones in that correspond to the emotions they are experiencing, which may contribute to their recovery or peaceful transition. I highly recommend using music therapy regularly with dementia patients. Ask a close family member which songs the patient grew up with and enjoyed, play the songs for them regularly, and watch what happens. You must realize that everything started with sound. Sound is food for the nervous system. Sound becomes light. The Bible states, "...in the beginning was the Word, and the Word was with God, and the Word was God…" You see, it all started with sound, which many believe, was the sacred sound Om. "…And God SAID, let there be light, and there was light…" Before light, there was sound. Mark my words: the future of medicine is sound. If you want to treat the root cause of a condition, go to where it all started, the beginning, which is sound. You can eat all of the healthy food you want, but you are still treating the condition from the symptoms/physical up. Why not start treating the condition from the top down. It is the "invisible world" that controls and directly affects the visible world. If you want to treat a condition from the top down, start with sound. The healing effects will cascade down to the subtle/light body, then to the mental body, then to the physical body. All aspects of the Self will be treated when one engages in music therapy.

These days most yoga studios will have periodic sound healings, which is a good place to start to experience the power of sound. Don't take my word for it. Go and try it! Go to a sound healing at your local yoga studio and see how your nervous system feels before and after. Solfeggio Harmonics, including the vibrations of 432hz, 528hz, and binaural beats are also excellent choices of sound for your nervous system. You can search YouTube or Spotify for these sounds and listen to them regularly to soothe your nervous system.

Nutritional Therapy for Alzheimer's

Please remember that the goal of treatment for Alzheimer's is to live a lifestyle and eat a diet that decreases neuroinflammation. It is helpful to avoid aluminum (often found in antiperspirants, antacids, and cookware). If symptoms start to appear, nutritional therapy can be helpful.

- Vitamin C: 500 to 1,00mg per day
- Vitamin E: 100 to 200 IU per day
- Fish oils: 1,000mg EPA + DHA per day
- Grape seed or pine bark extract (>95% procyanidolic content): 150 to 300mg per day

- Curcumin: found in turmeric formulations. Bioavailability is important, and brands should be researched carefully. I use Ron Teeguarden's Dragon Herbs activated curcumin, which can be purchased online.
- Theracurmin: 300mg per day
- Thiamine: 3-8g per day
- Phosphatidylserine: 100mg three times per day
- L-acetylcarnitine: 1,500mg per day
- Methylcobalamin: 1,000mcg upon waking up each day
- Melatonin: 3mg in the evening half hour before bedtime

Herbs

Lion's mane mushrooms – Lion's mane mushroom is a **very promising** treatment for Alzheimer's dementia. Preliminary studies are showing that it is neuroprotective, anti-inflammatory, and may be able to help prevent, reverse, or slow down cognitive decline. It has been shown in animal studies to increase nerve growth factor (NGF) as well as decrease production of amyloid beta (AB) protein. **If I had a parent or grandparent who was showing signs of mild cognitive impairment or who had been diagnosed with dementia, I would definitely recommend lion's mane 250mg three times daily.** Mushrooms are showing promise across the board to help with a multitude of health problems. For nerve related conditions, lion's mane is showing that it is here to help.

Please do your own research to find a brand that is bioavailable and from a trusted source. There are many mushroom companies out there that are not third party tested and it is important to find a good brand.

Ginkgo biloba – (24% ginkgo flavonglycosides): 240 to 320mg per day. Please do your own research, as there is a lot of evidence showing that gingko may be helpful for the brain.

CHAPTER 9:
ATTENTION-DEFICIT/
HYPERACTIVITY DISORDER

A. An Energetic Paradigm of ADHD

The mind will either follow the breath or the breath will follow the mind. ADHD occurs when the mind is scattered and leading the way.

Attention-deficit/hyperactivity disorder is a diagnosis made up by a group of psychiatrists working unconsciously or consciously under the direction of the pharmaceutical companies. This does to mean that the symptoms of ADHD are not real; the symptoms are real, and I am in no way trying to minimize the nature of the symptoms. The problem, however, is not a chemical imbalance in the brain, as smart advertisement would lead one to believe. ADHD is a multi-factorial condition stemming from many different causes. Just like with any other condition, it is important to identify as many of the causes and treat each cause at the root.

It is important to realize that each and every child and human being is unique. Those of you who study astrology understand that each person has specific unique abilities and interests as well as challenges. These specific gifts or challenges are designed in accordance with the human's purpose in this lifetime. When you try to take a child who is geared towards the artistic, left-brain-dominant creative endeavors and make him sit still in a crowded room, listening to lectures on analytical right-brained statistics he is not interested in, he will naturally have a hard time sitting still. This is true especially if the curriculum is scripted and uninspired. You see, this child was not designed to learn about mathematical statistics. Some children are also very intuitive and have a hard time listening to a scripted lecture. Some children can only learn from people who they look up to and respect. Not to minimize the value and wisdom of teachers, but each student may require a specific type of teacher to feel inspired and motivated. Also, no one ever sits down with these children, *teaching* them how to sit still and focus. Each child has unique abilities, and it is important to identify what they are, emphasize their strengths, and put them in an optimal environment to develop their gifts. There is a multitude of ways of finding one's astrologic charts. I highly recommend Universal Kaballah chart readings, as they can reveal a host of knowledge about oneself. Also, when parents can better understand themselves and their children, they can start working with Universal laws rather than abiding by an outdated, standardized educational system, which was not designed to strengthen the unique attributes of their children.

You must also consider the fact that we are living in an age of technology and mass stimulation. From an early age the child is bombarded with external stimuli to the point that they are continuously ingrained to being pulled away from their center to whatever stimuli is external. Therefore, it is vital to teach a child how to remain centered in spite of whatever external stimuli are pulling at their attention. This once again comes back to teaching children how to breathe in a calm, relaxed, manner, which will ground them into the present moment. This will also entrain their brain waves to be calm, relaxed, and open to the flow of Universal life force energy.

The brain waves of a child with ADHD correspond to the rhythm, amplitude, and rate of their breath. Therefore, someone with ADHD will have a scattered, highly variable, rhythm, rate, and depth of breath. The breath will be "all over the place." If one can learn how to entrain the breath to be relaxed and rhythmic, the brain waves will also entrain, and the person will be able to sit still and focus from the inside out rather than be pulled to whatever external stimuli or thoughts they are experiencing.

Diet also can be a contributing factor to hyperactivity. Too much sugar, or stimuli such as caffeine, can also contribute to a person's ability to pay attention and focus. As everybody already knows, sleep is vital for a person's overall energy as well as clearing the garbage out of the subconscious mind. Optimizing sleep and diet are essential parts of a comprehensive approach towards ADHD.

ADHD is more prevalent in people who live in big cities. This is because the energy of the city is one of constantly being on the "go." This creates a scattered lifestyle, leading to a brain with scattered brain waves. It is vital that no matter where one lives, they find time to relax, breathe, and connect with their higher Selves in their center.

B. Modern Western View and Treatment of ADHD

If you go to see a Western psychiatrist for ADHD, they will likely ask you a series of questions using a standardized rating scale, such as an adult Connor's rating scale (you can find this online), or follow the standard protocol of the *DSM-5*. After a short interview, the cautious ones may ask you to see a neuropsychologist, who will once again administer standardized questions depending on what rating scale they are using. If they find that you suffer symptoms of inattention, restlessness, daydreaming, inability to sit still, etc., in two or more settings with symptoms starting from an early age, they will likely place you on stimulant medications such as Ritalin, Adderall, Vyvanse, etc.

There are essentially two different subtypes of stimulant medication. Pharmaceutical companies take these two types and package them as different brand names, though they are essentially the same chemicals with different onset/duration of actions. Both subtypes work by increasing the availability of norepinephrine and dopamine in the synapses of the brain. The exact mechanism of action is largely unknown. It is hypothesized that Ritalin (methylphenidate subtypes) blocks the reuptake of norepinephrine and dopamine in extraneuronal spaces. The other subtype, such as Adderall (dextroamphetamine/amphetamine), supposedly not only blocks repute but also increases the release of norepinephrine ad dopamine.

Drugs such as Ritalin and Adderall are very similar in chemical make up to the street drug methamphetamine. The drugs are very effective at temporarily band-aiding symptoms of inattention. The user will often experience a rush of euphoria (dopamine effect, which is also what makes the drug addictive) as well as an increased ability to sit still and pay attention. However, after an initial period or rush of energy, the drugs will wear off and the person will often crash and feel tired and lethargic.

Imagine that each person is like a car. Each person has a limited amount of energy or gas. When one takes stimulants, it's like stepping on the gas pedal and revving the RPM up to redline. Yes, the person will go "faster," thus the word "speed." They may even be able to get more done in a shorter amount of time initially. However, the person will quickly burn up their energy and then "crash." Also, what happens to a car when one constantly steps on the gas and "red lines" it? The car, over a long period of time, will start to break down. The same goes for the nervous systems of humans. The medication activates the sympathetic nervous system, or the "fight or flight" response. It's like revving your system up to the point of tricking it into believing it's being chased by a bear. The human body is intelligently designed and capable of withstanding all kinds of acute stress; however, if the drug is taken daily over a long period of time, tolerance will be built. Higher doses will be needed, which will not achieve the desired effect. Pretty soon, one will start to feel abnormal if they don't have the medication. This is when addiction and dependence can happen. The whole while, the nervous system is being taxed. Chronic stress and inflammation will occur over a long period of time.

Also, it is important to know that two main side effects of stimulants are decreased appetite and a decreased need for sleep. These are the two primary ways the body renews its energy or "fills up its gas." So, not only is the medication burning up the gas, but it is also tricking the body into not filling up it's "gas" or energy from food and sleep. Thus, over a long period of time, the body starts to wear down and become addicted to the medication. Then the medication eventually stops working and tolerance is built. This whole time, nothing is being done to address the actual cause(s) of the symptoms.

Stimulants can sometimes be helpful for certain populations under certain short-term conditions. For example, there are times where one needs to step on the gas of their car to get somewhere really fast. For example, many college students will take stimulants during finals week, and it helps them. It helps them stay up, stay focused, and pass their tests. It helps them focus on jobs, books, and activities that they normally wouldn't be interested in. Yes, the body is damaged, but their bodies/cars are able to recover after finals when they stop taking the medication. It is important, however, to only take the medication consciously. This means if they are going to take stimulants that they set an intention, take the medication, clear out any distractions, and completely focus on the task at hand. It is also important to debunk the myth that ADHD medications need to be taken every single day. This is simply not true. If one is going to take stimulants, it is important to do so only when it is absolutely needed, with clear conscious intention and awareness of the risks. It is also important to note that it is illegal to take these drugs without their own prescription.

However, may it be said that if people were actually doing what they love and not following the conditioning of the system, ADHD wouldn't exist. This means that if people were to actually do something they loved and were naturally interested in, they wouldn't need help focusing because they would love what they are doing. However, because of the deep conditioning in society that children need to follow the script of classic Western education, college, and earn money in a "professional" job after college, there will continue to be children who are forced to study or take part in things they are not interested in or naturally inclined to. Therefore, while the children of the future are being forced to "fit in," they will need medications to try to fit in. It will take a paradigm shift in consciousness to see that each child was actually meant to stand out and not "fit in." Thus, the system will continue to perpetuate the diagnosis of ADHD, and the use of stimulant medications, and those at the top of the pharmaceutical companies will continue to benefit until a radical shift in consciousness happens starting at the "top."

C. Natural Treatment Approaches Towards ADHD

Breathwork for ADHD

Please see Breathwork for Anxiety section. I would recommend 4/7/8 breathing, along with regular box breathing. Continued, repetitive focus on the breath is the best way to calm an overactive, distracted mind.

I recommend downloading the Insight Timer application on your cellphone. Search for a mindfulness exercise that resonates with you. Practice this meditation regularly until you have the ability to sit still and focus on your breath for up to 10 minutes. This will help your inattention and scattered brainwaves.

Nutritional Therapy for ADHD

Foods to avoid: **Avoid all refined sugar** and food additives! Identify and avoid any allergenic foods and other foods that make you feel hyper, nervous, or ungrounded.

Magnesium: Magnesium helps in majority of cases (6mg/kg of body weight day) as does vitamin B6 (06mg/kg/day). 15mg Zinc 1-2 times per day in selected cases is effective. Taper off as improvement occurs, usually within three months. Zinc intake must also be balanced with copper. Fish oil 1-3g/day can also be effective.

Plant Medicine

Ibogaine – I would consider ibogaine as an option only when all other modalities have failed. I do not recommend this option for children, only for those adults who have tried everything else for ADHD and still have yet to find an effective solution. Ibogaine is a bark from a plant from West Africa. It is a powerful, potent, psychoactive plant that should be researched carefully before consumption. It has the consciousness of a gentle grandfather spirit. I will write more about it in Chapter 10 on Addiction, as it is a powerful tool for those who are suffering from opiate addiction.

It is, however, capable of "defragmenting" the mind, thus clearing up space. Think of your mind as an iPhone. Over the years, you have downloaded a multitude of applications, taken many photos, and now have no space, as applications are constantly running and you don't know where they came from or how to stop them. Thus, you are constantly running on past applications/programming, which invade the peace of the present moment. You need to clear up space or defragment your hard drive in your mind. Ibogaine, from my experience, is a powerful plant that is able to clear up space in your mind and quiet it. It is able to "delete" some of the applications running in your mind or at least show you where they were downloaded and how some programs may not be serving you any longer. After my experience with ibogaine, I was left with a quiet, peaceful mind and able to focus on whatever project I desired. I hope it can do the same for some who are called to it. Please remember, this plant is not for everyone. It is powerful. It is conscious. It is special and should only be entered into with the utmost reverence. It is a calling, and if you feel called to it, please feel free to do your own research to see if it is for you. You should be off of all psychiatric medications at least two weeks prior to entering into any journey. A trusted site to partake in ibogaine is listed here: ibogawellness.com.

CHAPTER 10:
ADDICTION

Addiction is not the problem. The problem is the body of pain usually stemming from trauma, which one attempts to cover up and appease with the addiction. So, as addiction specialist Gabor Maté states, the real question should be "...not what's the addiction, but what's the pain underneath..."

A. Addiction from a Spiritual Perspective

Most addictions are rooted in a lack of loving connection. Human beings are meant to be in connection with nature and with each other. When we have unresolved trauma and conditioned belief patterns which produce pain, we tend to produce feelings of guilt, shame, and fear, which cause us to isolate and seek solace in addictive behaviors to cover up the pain. Therefore, loving connection in a likeminded community is the best treatment for any type of addiction. This is why Alcoholics Anonymous has helped so many people for such a long time. Yes, the 12 steps help, but the real medicine is in the connections and support that is formed between the members and mentors. Having a group of like-minded and openhearted individuals who don't judge you and support you in your recovery is the best medicine. However, most addicts, because of the low vibratory state associated with their addiction, tend to isolate and seek solace in a mind-numbing activity or substance.

Most substances that people become addicted to are "pain" killers. This means that addiction stems from people trying to cover up some sort of physical or emotional pain, which can be traced back to some type of trauma that was experienced in the past. Dr. Gabor Maté has written several books, which explain this in detail. One book that I highly recommend is *In the Realm of Hungry Ghosts*. Human beings are not taught how to hold space for their emotional or physical pain; therefore, we seek solace in mind- or body-numbing substances or behaviors to escape the pain. However, when we try to escape the pain, we are actually causing more pain. So, we must learn how to control the breath and stay calm when the pain surfaces so that we don't try to escape. When we are able to hold space and not run from our pain, we will be able to develop a sense of compassion for ourselves and then for others. We will become aware of the root cause of the pain and eventually be able to recondition our brains to encompass the cause of pain with higher vibratory emotional states, such as compassion and forgiveness. This act will not be done just once, but every single time the pain surfaces. When we feel safe enough to simply be with the cause of our pain, we will learn how to transmute the emotional vibration of the pain into compassion and forgiveness, and eventually the pain will become a source of strength. Beneath every shadow or pain is a gift. Once we have integrated the root cause of the pain, we will be able to help people who are experiencing similar pain and speak to them from our hearts because we have the keys to the consciousness of how to integrate the pain. Then we will no longer associate fear/separation with the pain but feelings of love/connection and the fragmented parts of our souls, which we thought were not acceptable, are integrated back into the consciousness of wholeness. Then, the amygdala will begin to feel safe in the body and no longer seek to cover up the pain with addictive behaviors and substances.

B. Modern Westernized View and Treatment of Addiction

The *DSM-5* has a checklist of symptoms and qualifiers for addiction, which you can find if you search "DSM-5 addiction criteria" online. Roughly, addiction from a Western perspective it is described as "the continued use of a mood-altering substance or behavior despite adverse consequences." These substances and behaviors are attempts to provide, at first, immediate gratification, then, as time goes on, the relief of undesirable feelings or symptoms. From a biochemical perspective, there are many neurotransmitters that play a role in addiction. The main neurotransmitter that scientists believe is involved in addiction is dopamine.

Dopamine is the neurotransmitter that is released in the brain to make you feel motivation, focus, and pleasure. When you lack dopamine, you may start to feel a sense of apathy and depression. Most addictive behaviors release dopamine in the brain, which can at first produce a sense of mild euphoria. However, with continued use or abuse of the behavior or substance, the repetitive release of dopamine can cause a chemical addiction on a cellular level in the brain and body. Then the addicted one will seek the chemical or substance just to feel "normal." Tolerance is built, and the addictive behavior or substance no longer causes euphoria but reinforces the addiction to the point where one can't even feel normal without the addictive behavior or substance. However, to try to fix this problem with a pharmaceutical may temporarily cause alleviation in symptoms but in the long run will likely cause a further chemical imbalance. The drug or prescription may temporarily relieve symptoms but is in no way treating the root cause of the imbalance, which stems from unresolved trauma, pain, and a lack of loving connection.

Currently, in Western medicine, there are few effective medications that treat addiction. If you go see a psychiatrist for alcoholism, they may give you naltrexone, which may temporarily decrease cravings, or Antabuse, which will cause you to get physically sick if you drink, but these once again are not treating the addiction at the root cause.

It is ironic that many opioid abusers become addicted after they were placed on opioids by a doctor who prescribed them for pain. Then, once someone becomes addicted, the Western treatments tend to try to wean someone off of the opioid by giving suboxone or methadone, which are still opioids but in milder forms. In my clinical practice, I have found that suboxone and methadone can temporarily help someone by helping them get onto a "weaker" opioid. The side effects are less, and the patient is usually able to function better in society; however, they still are never able to reach their full creative potential and the taper usually takes a long time and requires consistent follow up. Many never complete the full taper. Many patients relapse, and I found rarely do these treatments actually successfully treat the root cause of the problem or even address the problem.

The Western treatment for other addictions usually involves long-term therapy, such as cognitive behavioral therapy, which seeks to identify negative thinking patterns and replace them with positive thinking patterns. This, however, does not work if the patient is not conscious at the moment of wanting to use. And it is difficult to be "conscious" and aware 24 hours a day. Western medicine once again seeks to tap into the analytical/thinking mind and solve the problem by trying to analyze it. However, by focusing on the problem, one is actually feeding it. Where attention goes, blood flows, and it grows. Scientifically, in the brain, every time you pay attention to a negative pattern, there is a neural pathway that is created or reinforced, like walking down a road over and over again. Pretty soon, the neural pathway is so ingrained that it becomes the easiest road to walk down, thus forming or reinforcing the problem. Yes, it is important to become aware of the conditioning and programming behind the addiction and to become aware when negative thoughts are creeping into the psyche; however, by focusing on it, one never cures it. Instead, the best way to replace negative conditioning is by not feeding it. By shifting attention to creating a new, healthier "addiction" or "habit" in its place, you create a new pathway/road that diverts the energy from the previous problem into a healthier road/habit/path. As you focus on this new habit consistently, the new pathway will become easier to walk down, and the old patterning will "starve," as you are not walking down that path or giving it attention.

C. Natural Treatment Approaches Towards Addiction

Community

As previously stated, a supportive, non-judgmental community where one feels safe to speak their truth is the best medicine for any sort of addiction. It is most often found within one's trusted circle or family. However, sometimes it is too difficult to be truthful regarding addiction to one's family, especially for those who feel as though they will be judged or shamed. In these situations, it can be helpful to find a community going through similar struggles.

Cigarette Addiction

John's Hopkins conducted a study, which shows promising results for psilocybin in helping with nicotine addiction (Johnson, Garcia-Romeu, Cosimano, & Griffiths, 2014).

I have witnessed stories of people who were lifelong cigarette smokers who were able to quit smoking easily after one journey with psilocybin. One might say they just had a "spiritual" moment, where their paradigm about life shifted and they woke up from their journey, and there was a "duh" moment. They realized life is amazing and beautiful and that they wanted to live, so they quit smoking on the spot.

I have also met many people and can personally testify that ibogaine has been very helpful for many seekers who wished to quit smoking. Iboga seems to be able to work on the part of the brain associated with addiction and can be helpful in many/most addictive compulsive behaviors.

I have also met personal shamanic practitioners who are having success using plant medicines to cure addiction. Ancient cultures, and anybody who's ever grown and tended to the tobacco plant, know that it is a sacred medicine/master plant. It is often times used in ayahuasca ceremonies (mapacho) for intention setting, protection, and to move energies. Through generations of societal conditioning and subconscious programming, it has become one of the most abused plant medicines in the world. However, if used properly in ceremony, tobacco has the potential to help with many conditions. Though it may sound counterintuitive, it may be possible to cure cigarette addiction by using tobacco with reverence and intention.

Opiate Addiction

My personal belief is that iboga is the future of treatment for opiate addiction. As any opiate addict or close friend or family member of a user knows, most opiate addicts want to be clean. They try to get clean numerous times, but the withdrawal symptoms are too severe, and they usually end up right back where they started.

What if there was a way to be free of opioid addiction without any withdrawals? What if nature provided a way to be free of one's addiction and be given a second chance at life without the withdrawal symptoms? Does it sound too good to be true? Well, in this particular case I believe that Mother Nature has provided a way in the form of iboga.

Ibogaine is plant native to Western Africa and was discovered by the Bwiti tradition when an African woman accidentally ingested the bark of the tree. She went on a psychoactive journey into her own psyche and discovered the plant had given her many spiritual insights. This led to the exploration of all the plant offered. The good news is that modern science is slowly starting to understand that some studies show that close to 80-90% of those who ingest the plant with the right intention and in the right set and setting are having miraculous recoveries from opioid addiction. It is a powerful plant and should only be used when called to use it in the right set and setting with a physician present. There have been cases of sudden death associated with its use but usually in a non-supervised use of the plant. It is still considered illegal in the United States; thus, most users will go to Costa Rica or another country where it is considered legal.

The reason I mention ibogaine as a potential treatment for heroin addiction is because in my journeys, I have met several trusted people who have successfully used ibogaine to get clean from heroin addiction. Their testimonies have inspired me to write about it. These people had tried every other Western treatment with no success but with ibogaine were given a second chance at life. If I had a family member or friend who was addicted to opioids, I would want to know about ibogaine.

Please be advised that ibogaine is not a cure-all. It shows potential for helping those not only addicted to heroin but also cocaine, nicotine, and alcohol, as well as many other substances. It seems to actively work on the centers in the brain related to addiction. Yes, ibogaine can reset addictive behaviors and work chemically on dopamine; however, if no changes are made after its ingestion, the patient will likely relapse! Therefore, it is vital to have a plan in place not only before entering into a relationship with the plant but also after. A supportive community, diet and exercise regimen, and meditation practice are all likely to be a helpful part of integration. Ibogawellness.com is a trusted site for those who feel called to work with the plant.

CHAPTER 11:
POST-TRAUMATIC STRESS DISORDER

A. PTSD from a Spiritual Perspective

Dr. Joe Dispenza has done amazing, scientific work with the mind/body connection, and the following section was inspired by his writings and my personal experience, which resonates with these teachings.

Post-traumatic stress disorder occurs when the body receives a shock of high emotional charge and stores this energy and memory in the mind and body. Because the body does not want to reexperience the trauma, it constantly lives in fear that the past event will happen again, which can cause anxiety, insomnia, fear, isolation, inflammation, and all kinds of resulting dis-eases. Many people who have experienced severe trauma no longer feel safe in their bodies and unconsciously disassociate or escape to appease the discomfort.

Trauma occurs when an event with very high emotional charge, whether conscious, subconscious, or unconscious, occurs. The mind takes a snapshot of the cause/event. The higher the emotional charge, the greater the charge of the memory associated with it. Then the body, along with the mind, remembers the unpleasant feeling and, to prevent it from happening again, produces stress hormones to prepare. This occurs until most people, on average 70% of the time, are in a past memory, in fear, afraid it's going to happen again so in a perpetual state of sympathetic activation/fight or flight, reactionary mode. When this is carried on for days, it becomes a mood; for months, a temperament; for a year, a personality; and for years, a character.

The body is the unconscious mind, so it doesn't know the difference between a past event and what is happening now, so the mind, when worried about the past trauma, then produces the exact same chemical messengers as it would if experiencing the past event; it fires and wires together in the same way until the same feelings produce the same thoughts and same thoughts produce the same feelings.

Then the familiar past is determining the predictable future. By the age of 35, we are running on subconscious automatic programs/habits/tracks 95% of the time. Though 5% of our conscious mind wants to change, we are stuck in our patterns of thought/behavior/action/conditioning.

However, we can access our subconscious minds through meditation and slow, relaxed, deep breathing, which lengthens and slows down the brain waves, thus activating the parasympathetic nervous system so that we can watch/observe the mind, enter the operating system, then through conscious intention, start sifting through, organizing, integrating, then reprogramming and upgrading the software on our operating system/brain.

If thoughts alone can trigger the stress response, then thoughts can also trigger the pleasure/reward response. So, actually, the best way to get rid of old programming/trauma is not by focusing on it, but when it comes up, acknowledge it, observe it, feel it, send it love, compassion, and forgiveness, then shift your attention to the future/desired goals/character/ habits you want to develop. Where attention goes, energy flows, and it grows. So instead of spending your entire day trying to cover up and suppress a road (neural pathway/habit) you've walked down a million times, you start creating a new path/road/neural pathway and continue to walk down it/redirect your attention to it consciously until the new road has been trampled upon so much that until it's easier to walk down than the old road/habit/trauma. And just like any road that hasn't been given attention, the old habit/trauma/road/neural pathway, when it's not fed, will eventually die off/be overgrown with weeds and no longer walked down.

Everyone has experienced some sort of trauma in his or her life. A good example would be an army veteran who returns from active combat. After witnessing many horrific events, and perhaps even being an active participant, he now has trauma stored in his mind/body. He has numerous triggers that will automatically activate the fear/sympathetic nervous system response. Any time he hears a loud noise, or sees a gun, etc., it can trigger the response that he is in danger. The emotional charge received from the traumas witnessed are ingrained on the psyche, mind, and in the body on a cellular level. Upon discharge and returning to the States, military members are expected to simply go back to normal civilian life. This is nearly impossible to do. The body, mind, and psyche has already been conditioned to be constantly on guard, and on top of that they now have witnessed and experienced numerous traumas, which are now ingrained into the body. Also, nobody has taught them how to come back into normal civilian life, and subconsciously everything still remains a threat. One cannot simply shut off the sympathetic nervous system without being taught how to do it. Thus, war veterans are often moved away from their brothers and sisters whom they have formed bonds with and left to try to reintegrate into a society that has not a clue what they have been through and thus can't understand them. This leads to isolation, addiction, and often times difficulty in the family to no fault of their own. Another simple example can be of a man who experienced a traumatic break up with his fiancée. Now every time he sees, hears, or smells anything that reminds his subconscious mind of her, his mind, thus body, is taken back to the traumatic experience. Because he doesn't want to reexperience this trauma, he now subconsciously walks around with a closed heart, unwilling and afraid to connect. This leads to isolation, which leads to inflammation, which leads to dis-ease.

B. Modern Western View and Treatment of PTSD

DSM-5 criteria for diagnosing PTSD include: the person being exposed to a stressor (death, threat of death, sexual violence, threat of or actual injury) either though experience or by witnessing/learning about the stressor; the person experiencing exposure symptoms (flashbacks, nightmares, unwanted memories, emotional distress regarding traumatic memories, and/or physical reactivity to these reminders); avoidance of trauma-related stimuli; negative alterations in mood, thoughts, and feelings about the world (may include self-blame, isolation, blame of others, forgetting aspects of the trauma, negative worldview, etc.); changes in arousal and reactivity (may include destructive behavior, risky behavior, heightened irritability/aggression, hypervigilance, difficulty concentrating, difficulty sleeping, etc.). For a diagnosis of PTSD, the symptoms must have persisted for more than one month, must be due to the stressor itself and not due to a substance or illness, and must cause distress or impairment in the person's life (socially, at work, etc.) (Diagnostic and Statistical Manual of Mental Disorders, Fifth Edition, 2013).

As you can see, the criteria try to fit a unique soul into a checklist of symptoms. If the symptoms seem to fit, you are labeled with a lifelong chronic condition called post-traumatic stress disorder. This label is with you for life. Not to mention that this checklist of symptoms was made by mostly well-meaning psychiatrists who unknowingly are being entrained by the people at the top of the pyramid scheme.

Psychiatrists usually will diagnose you with PTSD after a quick interview, where they run off a checklist of symptoms. If you have the symptoms, you will likely be diagnosed and placed on medications that don't treat the cause but attempt to band-aid the symptoms. Even if the medications temporarily numb the symptoms, the symptoms can always return given the proper trigger as the root cause was not identified or addressed.

The standard treatment in the Western world for PTSD is to give an SSRI medication, such as Lexapro, Paxil, Prozac, Celexa, or an SNRI, such as Effexor, Cymbalta, etc. The symptoms may be temporarily numbed, but these medications do not cure PTSD, cause other side effects, and actually make it more difficult to actually treat the root cause, as you will be numbed down and unable to exercise your judgment, willpower, and intuition. For nightmares and dreams, some psychiatrists will use an anti-hypertensive medication, such as prazosin, which antagonizes peripheral alpha-1 adrenergic receptors. Some patients can have a decrease in intensity and frequency of the nightmares, but this relief is usually temporary.

An intuitive reader will by now have realized that the world of Western medicine uses SSRIs for almost every single psychiatric condition. They are used for depression, anxiety, postpartum depression, peri-menopausal symptoms, PTSD, etc. This goes to show that nobody really knows what is going on biochemically or even how the medications are working. All they know is that it temporarily disturbs the neurotransmitter makeup of the body, which can sometimes effectively numb the symptoms.

C. Natural Treatments for PTSD

Plant medicine, daily, consistent breathwork and meditation, subconscious mind healing, harmonium healing, and Naam meditation for dreams and nightmares are all effective, natural treatments for PTSD.

Best Medicine for PTSD

I believe that science will slowly realize that a **daily, consistent breathwork program** is the best treatment for trauma. Please remember that the best way to calm down in any situation is to regulate the brain waves through the breath. Therefore, one can utilize the 4/7/8 breath or box breathing in any given situation when the trauma arises to realize a calm internal state. For chronic trauma, transformational breathwork and the three-part breath technique (David Elliott trains in this specific type of breath) are two ways of accessing the trauma through the breath. The goal is not to "get rid" of the trauma but to change the emotional charge associated with the it through conscious breathing and therapy.

If you have a trusted guide, theta healing may be another way to access the trauma and change the emotional charge associated with it. Another way of dealing with PTSD is to optimize the pranic body through a daily, consistent pranayama practice. I have training in these modalities, and you can reach out for 1:1 sessions or to be given a specific, daily pranayama practice to optimize your pranic body. Please realize that when the pranic/subtle body is optimized through daily consistent breathwork, the trauma will be subdued, as the higher energy vibration that the subtle body is vibrating at will entrain the lower frequency emotions associated with the trauma.

Please realize that when one is in a theta brain wave state (usually right before falling asleep, upon awakening, or when in meditation), one is more open and suggestible, and the subconscious mind is accessible. This is when we can access the trauma, as the fear associated with it will be quelled. Once the trauma is accessed, one can forgive the trauma and start to associate a different emotional charge to it. The trauma can oftentimes be accessed once the analytical, thinking mind (ego) is out of the way. This can be done with simple breathing techniques or with plant medicine. Theta healing is one modality that works to access the theta brain waves and can be helpful for some individuals.

Treatment for Nightmares

There is emerging evidence that CBD oil may be used for REM sleep suppression in PTSD for those suffering from reoccurring nightmares. It may be helpful to take CBD oil 30 minutes prior to bedtime to suppress nightmares. Recept by Prime My Body is the brand that I work with and recommend.

Recommendations for PTSD

Food
- Avoid caffeine, alcohol, and refined carbohydrates.
- Eat regular, planned meals in a relaxed environment.

Lifestyle
- Identify stressors and eliminate or reduce all sources of stress.

- Identify negative coping patterns and replace them with positive ones.
- Perform relaxation/breathing exercises for a minimum of five minutes twice a day.
- Exercise regularly.

Nutritional Supplements

- Calcium: 1,000mg/day
- Magnesium: 350 to 500mg/day
- Vitamin D3: 2000 to 4000 IU per day
- Vitamin B6: 25 to 50mg per day
- Folice acid: 800mcg per day
- Vitamin B12: 800mcg per day
- Fish Oil: 1000 to 3000mg EPA + DHA per day
- Flaxseed oil: 1tbsp per day

Herbs

- Kava: 45 to 70mg kavalactones three times per day

Ibogaine – I believe ibogaine can be an effective treatment for certain cases of post-traumatic stress disorder. Where all Western treatments have had minimal success, many veterans report clarity of mind and heart after experiencing the sacred plant medicine. The sacred plant has the ability to "defragment" the brain of traumatic memories. It can decrease the fear or negative emotions associated with the trauma and help the seeker understand where the trauma comes from. It is a very promising treatment for those who suffer from severe Post Traumatic Stress Disorder. Please read about it in Chapter 10 on Addiction.

Alternative Treatments

Eye movement desensitization and reprogramming – EMDR is a promising treatment for PTSD. Some holistic practitioners consider it a sacred practice. The mechanism of how it works is unknown. As the client is instructed to move their eyes bilaterally under the instruction of the practitioner, traumatic memories are consciously brought to surface. As the seeker continues to move their eyes, the trauma is experienced internally along with the emotions and bodily sensations. Continued treatments in conjunction with mindful breathing and eye movements seem to decrease the emotional charge associated with the trauma and in some cases release the trauma completely. Some trusted practitioners report miraculous success with this process. It is vital to find a practitioner with pure intentions, who holds loving space and believes that the treatment will work.

CHAPTER 12:
DEATH AND GERIATRIC CARE

A. A Spiritual Perspective of Death

Death is a transition state in consciousness, and there are ways to guide our elderly population into a peaceful transition.

Energy is neither created nor destroyed. If everything is energy, including the psyche or soul, then even a child can understand that the soul never dies. Through history, society has adopted the viewpoint that death is the ultimate thing to be feared and avoided, when in all reality death is simply changing energy forms and transitioning to a different state of consciousness. Thus, Western medicine has been able to make a fortune off of this fear-based belief system. Unfortunately, Western medicine has created a health care system that has made death the enemy; it treats symptoms and attempts to prolong life no matter the suffering or situation. Instead of promoting quality of life, it promotes quantity of life. It also makes a fortune off of cosmetics and products that are supposed to prevent aging. I believe the right question to ask is: how can we help those facing "death" enjoy the quality of their remaining days, transition, and change energy forms with a peaceful heart and minimal suffering? Some spiritual systems believe that the psyche will have a difficult time transitioning after death if they are stuck in attachment to the physical plane or things of the physical plane. As it seems, the Creator or Source of the Universe honors free will and choice, thus if the psyche is attached to things on the physical plane, that choice is honored.

In Chapter 43 of the book *Autobiography of a Yogi*, Paramhansa Yogananda is visited by his teacher Sri Yukteswar, who gives an informative account of what "the other side" or astral world is like. It is important to understand that he describes the astral world from his own belief system and perspective and that he also mentions that the Creator of the Universe is creative enough to honor each person's own unique belief system.

Those who have had a near death experience often describe the sensation of the psyche leaving the ego and body behind and merging with pure consciousness, which is often times described as pure white light or Source. Sometimes, it seems the psyche is given a choice as to whether it wants to leave or remain. The curious soul can read more about near death experiences at nderf.org. Anita Moorjani has also written a beautiful, descriptive, and relevant book that describes her experience entitled *Dying to Be Me*.

Those who have experienced "toad medicine," scientifically referred to as 5-MeO-DMT (5-methoxy-N,N-dimethyltryptamine), often describe an experience that is very similar to a near death experience. Although some have very difficult experiences on the medicine, many describe it as if the ego or body has left, and the psyche consciously rises above the body and merges with pure consciousness, which is sometimes referred to as a white light or Source. It is often described as a state of pure bliss and peace. Although the experience usually lasts less than 30 minutes, some will burst into tears upon returning to their bodies. It can sometimes be tears of joy to know where they come from, and sometimes it can be tears of sadness. Some are left with an epiphanic knowing that this life is a gift and that it is a privilege to be alive. However, 5MeO-DMT is not for everybody and should be carefully researched and investigated prior to use, as it is often highly mystical. **Who you work with is very important**, as is your intention, your energy, and the set and setting. It is also illegal in most countries. There are case reports of people who have worked with supposed shamans who have had very traumatic experiences, so please research guides and practitioners prior to taking this medicine.

Near death experiences and 5MeO-DMT are just a few examples of facing "death." These examples are cited to help the experiencer realize that there are alternative views of what death really is. If we can change our paradigm towards death, then we can change our attitude towards death and perhaps our attitude towards life. Once one knows and has experienced the "death particle," then they are not nearly as afraid of death and can live their lives with passion, gratitude, and fearlessness. Modern science is and soon will be discovering that science and consciousness are one and the same. This veil that has been placed between the two will slowly be lifted as global consciousness starts to raise its vibration. Quantum physicists are starting to explore what they term the "God particle." Many experiencers of ayahuasca are unknowingly experiencing the "death particle." These energy forms are so mysterious that science has yet to be able to properly explain them. Thus, the truth is that spirituality or consciousness has to be experienced, and words are sometimes inadequate to describe the actual experience. However, once someone has experienced the science of the energy behind these particles, it is truth for them, and the divine spark has been lit. What you know, you cannot not know. What you have experienced, you cannot deny.

Once one has experienced the infinity of the soul, they will slowly be desensitized to the stigma of death. This will lead to living life with purpose and passion without fear. This will also lead to a gradual shift in paradigm to be able to see death as a natural part of nature—as a leaf that "dies" every autumn; however, the tree (soul/psyche) remains.

B. Westernized View and Treatment of Death/End of Life

The current state of health care in the United States for our parents and grandparents could use an upgrade. I spent a year as a geriatric psychiatrist working as an attending physician for our elderly population. They are isolated, fed inflammatory food, and not exposed to natural healing modalities. Most lead psychiatrists who work in these facilities are so busy competing to accumulate patients for material gain that they seldom have time to connect with their patients. Instead, most of our elderly population are neglected and seen as a "number" for selfish financial interests. The psychiatrists who are successful in this realm are good businessmen but are not able to or unwilling to actually treat their patients except with medications that "shut them up" to keep them from causing any problems. The system is currently set up to try to preserve life with suffering rather than help our elderly population transition with grace, ease, and peace. Whenever a patient screams out for help, or in discomfort, the psychiatrist is immediately called to "shut them up" by giving them more medications. No time is given to investigate why the person may be truly calling out for help, as many in this population are not able to effectively communicate verbally. They are, however, trying to communicate energetically. Someone who has time and is intuitive can usually discover what the real cause of the cry for help is and assist.

I also spent time working in the skilled nursing facilities where many of our grandparents and parents wind up. The staff is overworked, the air is contaminated, and there is no space for real integration and healing. The system is set up so the doctors get paid based on the quantity of patients they see rather than the quality of service they provide. Many end up wasting away their final hours in an environment that is not conducive to peace or healing. The system also likes to drain the elderly person of their life savings prior to providing government support. For example, the government will only provide skilled nursing facility care after the financial resources of the patient is below as certain dollar amount. Thus, some elderly patients spend their entire lives following a system that encourages them to accumulate money and resources, only to have it drained back into the system at expensive care facilities.

The good news is there are treatments that can help. All that is needed is an increase in consciousness in the collective and a few like-minded people who are able to put aside their differences and come together for the common goal of helping our geriatric population transition with grace and ease.

I had the good fortune of being able to travel to Belize. While I was in a small town in Belize, I asked about what they do with the geriatric "psychiatric" population. The response I received was simple but profound. The town had no need for a psychiatrist. The geriatric population was housed on a "farm-like" area in nature. Each day, they spent time outside in the sunshine and fresh air. They were given food to eat from the earth. They listened to happy music from their childhood. Family members were allowed to come and visit with them, and there were optional activities during the day for human connection. With these modalities alone, they said it was extremely rare to have any psychiatric problems amongst the population.

C. Alternative Approaches Towards End-of-Life Care

Plant Medicine

Psilocybin (Magic Mushrooms) – My intuition tells me that psilocybin may be a beautiful tool to help our elderly population transition to the "other side" with dignity, grace, and without fear. John's Hopkins has completed a successful study with psilocybin and those with terminal cancer (Griffiths, et al., 2016).

When done in a formal ceremony with the right intention, set, and setting, the plant will reveal to the seeker that death is an illusion and that the soul never dies. This realization is something that must be experienced and cannot be explained in words. Though the brain of a patient with dementia, a relatively common illness in the elderly population, may not be properly working on the third dimensional level, the soul is still intact, which means it can still experience the plant medicine. It is a fact that dementia patients still retain musical memory on a cellular level. The magic mushrooms also help the brain form synapses and new neural connections, which help the experiencer see life and death from a new perspective. When the right music, intention, set, and setting is combined, psilocybin can help the experiencer experience ego death, where the analytical mind is no longer "in the way" and the fear and illusion of death can fall away. Scientific studies confirm that most who experience psilocybin consistently state that it was one of the top "spiritual" experiences of their lives. Death is a spiritual experience. Ask any person who has had a near death experience, and they can tell you that it highly spiritual. Plant medicines can help you see the illusion behind death and help you dissolve the fear associated with death. This fear has been built up through generations and generations of societal conditioning. As the illusion of death fades away, it can be seen as a gift. It can be seen as a transition state of consciousness. It can be seen as a temporary resting space and time for the soul. And thus, it can be entered into with grace, with ease, and even with joy. Death is not to be feared. It is a natural process in the evolution of life.

Please note that plant medicine is only one tool to help the experiencer experience death before death. Ego death can be achieved simply through deep meditation as one blends into "All that is," sometimes referred to as the quantum field in physics. All experienced meditators or sages of the past have achieved a state of disassociation from the ego simply through the breath.

You can change your mood/energetic frequency in less than 10 minutes. Low-vibration emotions, such as guilt, shame, and depression, can be transformed to high-vibration emotions, such as excitement or joy, within 10 minutes. Here's a breathwork video that I practice to shift my energetic frequency.

CHAPTER 13:
MISCELLANEOUS ITEMS

A. Couples Counseling

99% of all marital problems or disagreements are simply because of a lack of soul-to-soul communication. I truly believe we could cut the divorce rate in half by simply taking 10 minutes each evening to connect souls and communicate (Please remember, the word soul can be replaced with conscious awareness, God, Higher Self, etc.). However, this takes vulnerability, commitment, and intentional time. It needs to be a priority.

My recommendation to all couples, especially those who may be going through marital problems, is simple: Dedicate 10 minutes a night for soul-to-soul communication. It is good to verbally acknowledge the common intention prior. The rules of communication include: no attacking, no defending, and no blaming; the aim is to simply to express how one feels. The intention is simple: to communicate.

The soul is connected in three ways. Make eye contact (the eyes are the window to the soul). There are energetic lines, which connect the eyes to the heart. Hold hands (hands are connected via meridians to the heart). Take three slow deep breaths together ("eskimo kiss" by pressing your noses together and breathing together). Inhale to a count of four seconds and exhale to a count of seven seconds. Once the souls are connected, each person gets to choose one five-minute "song." This is sacred time for each person to express everything that is on his or her heart. That means the other partner cannot talk during this five minutes! They simply must maintain eye contact and listen with the intention of understanding what the other person is saying. Once one partner is finished, the other partner will then pick their "song" and have the floor for five minutes. This partner shouldn't use this time to respond to what was said; he/she should simply communicate whatever it is that is in his/her heart.

I truly believe that 10 minutes an evening of soul-to-soul communication will help in all areas of a relationship. However, if one partner wants to "hide" something in the relationship, this is difficult to do, as the truth will be exposed. But, the "truth" will set you free. And it is difficult to hide the truth when two souls are connected with a common intention of speaking their truths.

B. How to Safely Taper off of SSRI Medications

As previously mentioned, it is important to find a good, trusted doctor to safely taper off of SSRI medications. When tapered too quickly, SSRIs can cause "withdrawal symptoms," also known as "discontinuation syndrome." This can include symptoms such as lethargy, "brain zaps," depression, changes in sleep patterns, GI disturbance, and more. Sometimes the "brain zaps" can be alleviated by fish oil supplements.

When someone wants to wean off of an SSRI, it is a good idea to add a natural serotonin-boosting agent. In my clinical practice, I have had success using 5-HTP 50-100mg 30 minutes before bed with vitamins B6, B12, and folate. Depending on how long you've been on the medications, the taper schedule will be different. However, a good general rule of thumb is to taper off of the medication slowly. Please be advised, there is usually no rush to get off the medications. So, decreasing the medication by approximately 20% of the dose every 2-4 weeks is a good taper plan, depending on how long you've been on the medication. Magnesium 300-600mg may also be helpful to decrease the "brain zaps."

Daily use of CBD oil can also help appease the withdrawal symptoms of a taper.

C. A Word on Sleep

Sleep is vital for mood, a healthy mind, energy, etc. The mind cleans out its excess subconscious "garbage" while it sleeps. The body and mind also restore themselves to optimal levels during sleep. For those who struggle to fall asleep, please do a simple google search on "sleep hygiene."

Each person has a unique circadian rhythm, which follows the rising and setting of the sun. For those suffering from sleep problems, it would be a great practice to sun gaze during the "golden hours." This means within the hour of the sun rising and the last hour before it is setting. Sun gazing is not only one of the most powerful spiritual practices one can engage in but will also reset your circadian rhythm and help your sleep cycle by tuning your pineal gland, therefore all of your hormonal systems, including melatonin.

For those struggling to fall asleep, please do not let your physical eyes see any blue screen light one hour before bedtime. Also, please have a nighttime routine one hour before bed, which includes no phone or television programming. For the body to fall asleep, the mind must fall asleep. The quickest way to quiet the mind is through calm, rhythmic breathing. A good routine would be to put the cell phone and computer in a separate room and do a 20-minute guided yoga nidra practice before bed. Yoga nidra is sometimes referred to as yogic sleep. You can access yoga nidra meditations by downloading the free phone application Insight Timer. For those still struggling to sleep, it may be helpful to take the following supplements:

- GABA: 100-200mg 30 minutes before bedtime
- Melatonin: 3-6mg 30 minutes before bedtime
- 5-HTP: 100-200mg 30 minutes before bedtime

How to Reprogram Your Subconscious Mind While You Sleep

Have you ever noticed that when you try positive affirmations during the course of a busy day, they don't seem to register? This is usually because in the middle of the day you are in beta brain waves, sympathetic activation, and not open and suggestible. Your subconscious mind is running on programming and not open to new suggestions.

However, right before you fall asleep and wake up, your brain waves will gradually enter into the brain wave patterns of theta and delta, where it will be open and suggestible.

Therefore, if you live a busy life and would like to program your subconscious mind to abundance, joy, wealth, and harmony, it would be advisable to listen to subconscious mind reprogramming affirmations while you fall asleep and let it play throughout the night.

Dr. Bruce Lipton has a good video clip, which explains how this process works. You can find the video "Dr. Bruce H. Lipton Explains How To Reprogram The Subconscious Mind" on YouTube.

Please note that this is a powerful tool. 99% of all people who walk into the psychiatric office do so because of their beliefs in the programming and conditioning of their subconscious minds. By the age of 35, 95% of all an adult does is the result of subconscious programming. It is tremendously difficult to change for the better until the subconscious mind is reprogrammed. Therefore, it would be wise to listen to the type of programming/messaging you would integrate while you sleep.

Try this practice for two months and see if you have positive results, and please remember it is the unconscious, subconscious mind that produces thoughts, which lead to emotions, which lead to behaviors, habits, personality, and character. You can reconfigure from the top down by addressing your subconscious mind.

D. Traumatic Brain Injury

Traumatic brain injury can manifest with a wide variety of symptoms, and it is very difficult to predict when or what symptoms will appear. I have personally seen people with TBI suffer from depression, bipolar disorder, PTSD, anxiety, and even psychosis. Currently, in the Western psychiatric model, the only treatment that one can receive from a psychiatrist is symptom management using pharmaceutical drugs.

Once again, this is not correcting the actual cause of the condition, and even the symptomatic treatment will not last, as tolerance to the medications is built and the body adjusts.

Dr. Mark Gordon has thoroughly researched the realm of TBI and is doing amazing work helping those with TBI. I have personally attended one of his seminars and learned a lot about treating TBI by optimizing hormone levels in the body. Dr. Gordon is having a lot of success using this method, and if I had a family member with TBI, I would certainly give this modality a shot. Many seem to respond rapidly to hormone optimization, recover, and even thrive. By getting a thorough hormone evaluation, one can deduce which part of the brain might have been injured and provide the optimal neuro-permissive environment in the brain for it to start healing itself.

Another modality that may help those with TBI is called hyperbaric oxygen therapy (HBOT). Please do your own research to see if it may be a good fit for you or your family member.

E. Making the Unconscious and Subconscious Mind Conscious

Holotropic Breathwork

This is a great practice for people who are seeking to make their subconscious/unconscious mind conscious without the aid of plant medicines. Seekers can obtain supernormal levels of consciousness through this breathwork and can also heal deep-seated trauma.

Please be advised that this practice is powerful and should not be initiated if one feels unstable, as it can make the subconscious/unconscious mind conscious and destabilize you even further. It should only be practiced in a controlled environment, when the psyche is relatively stable and open to exploring consciousness.

LSD was first created to be studied as a model to see what was happening biochemically during psychosis. Dr. Groff reports that he volunteered to undergo LSD treatment to experience what it felt like to be in the shoes of his patients. Instead he ended up having a very powerful mystical experience, where he became pure consciousness. Since then, he has taught holotropic breathing, which helps people obtain non-ordinary states of consciousness. Holotropic breath, played alongside rhythmic spiritual music, will often times induce a state where the seeker can connect through the breath to his/her own psyche, or Spirit, and find the answers and integration he/she is seeking. This occurs as the unconscious and subconscious belief systems are brought into consciousness and experience; thus, the symptoms are alleviated as the unconscious is made conscious. Experiencers will often times also be able to clear past traumas and reprogram beliefs that are not in alignment with their primal unconditioned psyches. These supernormal states have long been often induced in shamanic cultures for initiation into shamanism and also for integration and healing of normal people. One can arrive in such a state, experience ego death, and merge with pure consciousness. Becoming "one with all that is," the quantum field, is a familiar concept to all spiritual backgrounds, including Buddhism, Hindiusm, Sufism, Kabbalism, Christian Mysticism, and most cultures that have not adopted the Western approach towards science. Dr. Groff goes on to explain that currently there is no difference in Western psychiatry between mystical experiences versus psychosis. He explains that these mystical states are actually supernormal, complementary experiences rather than abnormal distortions of reality, which would be labeled as psychosis. In the Western world, all great mystic yogis of the past would be labeled as psychotic, put on medications, and placed into inpatient psychiatric hospitals, including the Buddha, Jesus, St. Theresa, St. John of the Cross, and others.

For information on how to do holotropic breathwork, you can search for it on YouTube.

Resources to Change Your Subconscious Mind

The mind learns through repetition but needs to be in an open, suggestible brain wave state. Positive affirmations only work when we are present, open, and suggestible to the truth we want to implant into our minds. Western medicine encourages talk therapy, but by simply analyzing and focusing on the problem, it will not solve the problem but actually feed energy to it.

The majority of all people are running on subconscious programming. Subconscious beliefs lead to unconscious thoughts, which lead to undesirable feelings, which leads to transcription of proteins and hormones in alignment with that feeling. Most subconscious belief patterns are programmed from the ages of birth to seven years old, and by age 35, most experts believe we are operating on at least 95% subconscious programming. Therefore, in order to change one's life, it is important to change one's subconscious belief patterning.

Dr. Bruce Lipton does amazing work in this area. Please remember that if you can change your subconscious belief patterns, this will change your thought patterns, then your emotions, then your actions and speech, and then your habits, then your personality, then your character, then your destiny. Dr. Lipton's website has great resources that can lead you to the right system for you.

CHAPTER 14:
SYNCHRONIZATION, RHYTHM, ORCHESTRATION

SCIENCE IS THE MODERN LANGUAGE OF SPIRITUALITY. HERE'S SOME SCIENCE...

This chapter was written by guest author Dr. Ellie Wright

Neuroinflammation and Mental Health

As a naturopath physician, I am fascinated with the body's innate rhythm and the synchronization between cells, organs, neurotransmitters, and hormones. Our bodies have a natural synchronicity, and when functioning well, the body works like a clock.

I received holistic training in medical school at Southwest College of Naturopathic Medicine, where I studied the science of natural medicine as well as the allopathic approach to medicine. I specialized in determining connection between clinical observations and scientific research.

In addressing mental health, I strive to incorporate variety of approaches and modalities and discover the root cause of the problem, then work at the problem from the root up. I found great support in psychoneuroimmunology research because it offers a holistic approach to health through the interaction of gut health, mental health, immune system health, cytokines, neurotransmitters, and wellbeing.

In my approach to mental health and health in general, I focus on reducing inflammation through detoxification, resetting the circadian rhythm, balancing neurotransmitters, and intermittent fasting. I have been working in medical centers that focus on water fasting, juicing, and raw sprouting, detoxing with saunas, and tapering patients off drugs. I have noticed significant differences in patients' health after botanical medicine treatment, neurotransmitter therapy, ozone therapy, and nutritional therapy.

For me, genetic testing has become a routine starting point before any treatment is prescribed—in order to understand how to prepare the body before/after detox, what supplements need to be given, and in what therapeutic order to proceed with treatment. Epigenetics provides insight for methylation therapy and nutritional therapy for mental health. Methylation issues are present in most psychiatric conditions.

In my treatments, I have a therapeutic order of addressing inflammation, which starts with the bottom of the pyramid—detoxification, healing the gut, modifying gene expression by redirecting the pathways, balancing mTOR with autophagy, feeding the neurotransmitter pathways, and addressing nutritional deficiencies.

My evaluations start with determining oxidative stress, amino acid levels, fatty acid imbalance, glucose dysregulation, toxic overload, candida, zinc deficiency, vitamin B deficiency, bacterial overload, neurotransmitters, and hormonal imbalances, as every single one of these factors affects mental health. Almost every drug causes gut dysbiosis and nutritional deficiencies. For example, with Metformin, esomeprazole, and ranitidine, there is a resulting B12 deficiency. Heavy metal overload has been found to weaken the blood-brain barrier, alter neurotransmitter levels, and reduce glutathione. Copper overload, especially, has been found to be implicated in many mental disorders.

All of my treatments are personalized according to body type, sensitivities and intolerances, age, immune system, genetics, environmental exposure, and length of using certain drugs. However, the therapeutic order to health must be respected in order for the treatment to work.

Inflammation has been linked with every possible condition, from the cold, autoimmunity, hypertension, liver disease, weight, neurodegeneration, cancer, and psychiatric disorders. The key to reducing inflammation is regular detox that can be accomplished through intermittent fasting, anti-inflammatory diet, elimination diet, sauna, and other therapeutic modalities. Diseases are correlated with mitochondrial disfunction, high oxidative stress, and highly inflammatory markers with decreased function of SOD 1,2,3 (decrease detoxification). Inflammation in the brain has been correlated with increased interleukin IL-1 (in depression), IL-6 (in anxiety), TNF (in hostility and aggression), and an elevated quinolinic pathway. Aging comes with increased in oxidative damage in the brain, but higher levels of oxidative damage correlated to inflammation are more prevalent in mental disorders. Neuroinflammation translates to anxiety, depression, bipolar disorder, schizophrenia, and dementia.

The first step to approaching mental health problems is reducing overall inflammation by focusing on anti-inflammatory thoughts. The quality of your thinking determines the quality of your life. Practices, such as prayers, meditation, and deep abdominal breathing and spending time outdoors in the natural sunlight promote a change in the mental state. Love is best medicine, and laughter is best therapy. Studies suggest that laughter increases NK (natural killer cells) and antibodies and decreases pro-inflammatory cytokines. The universe is spiritual in essence, and everything starts with a thought and an emotion. A strong immune system starts with a peaceful mind. We heal in the parasympathetic and unconscious state. We can allow ourselves to enter into a healing mode and we can allow ourselves to act to our highest good and live in the moment of transformation and growth. Coming to terms with the unconscious is the medicine of the soul. It is a mental diet where we relax to become mindful. We need a vision for health, and we construct that through language. We heal through words, images, art, music, dance, and love.

I use self-hypnosis for self-discovery, self-healing, and self-knowledge because it reduces the gap between conscious and unconscious. We live in a holographic universe, and believing is mostly an unconscious act. To make the unconscious information conscious, we need vision and faith. When we start to heal, we turn dysfunctional experiences into functional experiences. In the process we overcome the subconscious resistance after soaking in vital mental thoughts. The emotional health comes from facilitating the release of emotions and applying the principle of gratitude. Yes, a mental diet is needed through relaxation, wakening of the mind, self-understanding, healing, and transformation. The transformation comes from removing blockages of negative emotions and allowing ourselves to come to term with inner self. Always seeking the unconscious (the other part of us that is asleep) through prayers, meditations, writing, painting, music, and active imagination. Through mental therapeutic approaches we integrate our inner world to outer world. Language can guide us inside of ourselves and guide us out. Words are spiritual guides, and positive affirmations are best tools to reprogram the mind. As Jacque Lacan said, symptoms are words trapped in the body. We become happy by studying happiness; therefore, there is a synchronicity in "breathing" your way to happiness. The same principle can be applied to health; we become healthy by emerging ourselves in healthy thoughts and practices. The success factor for mental health is finding the purpose, goals, and passions in life that engine the force to move forward.

The Orchestra of Neurotransmitters

Dopamine in the brain (misregulated in autoimmunity) it is a "motivator" neurotransmitter in the sense that it releases mental energy. Increased positive, rewarding relations was found to stimulate dopamine in the brain. Stimulating the dopaminergic pathway helps regulate pituitary hormones and support endocrine feedback loops. There are certain plants and nutrients that support dopamine production, and one of them is lemon balm. Ongoing studies suggest an increase in serotonin in the brain may lead to a decrease of dopamine. Dopamine regulates the release of insulin from the pancreas and norepinephrine from blood vessels. Elevated dopamine has been correlated with worry, impulsiveness, aggressivity, and attention deficits. Botanical medicine like Vitex stimulates the pituitary, which stimulates a further dopaminergic release. Again, it has been found that inflammation can decrease dopamine synthesis; in particular, certain gut bacteria (Clostridium difficile) interferes with its synthesis. L-Tyrosine plays a role in promoting healthy neurotransmitters, as it is the precursor of catecholamine, including dopamine, epinephrine, and norepinephrine. Tyrosine needs B6, vitamin C, and SAMe to convert to dopamine (caution when giving it if Clostridia is present). Histamines stimulate mood, thought, and the day/night rhythm of the brain. Histamine levels in the blood determine the undermethylation and overmethylation status. With increase in food allergies, there is elevated histamine, which leads to an increase electrical activity in the brain. Histamine stimulates dopamine in the brain.

GABA & Serotonin

Gaba plays a role in relaxation, sleep, and focus and decreases with aging. Lower concentrations are also found in post-menopausal, depressed women. Many plant-based nutrients and amino acids are supporting the synchronous production of neurotransmitters. Research suggests that GABA enhances serotonin. Everything is in a ratio in the body and works in a synchronic rhythm. It is necessary to understand and supplement only when necessary because high GABA means difficulty concentrating, fatigue, and sleepiness. 90% – 95% of serotonin is made in the gut with the support of healthy microbiota; the first step in addressing mental health starts with gut. When gut bacteria are compromised (yeast, fungus, bacteria overgrowth), I address this disbalance by recommending specific probiotics: Bacteroides fragilis, Lactobacillus helveticus, and Bifidobacterium longum (30 days). Research suggests that neurotransmitters work in synchrony with each other; when one is high, it causes the other to go low. It has been found that serotonin in the brain is enhanced by GABA and inhibited by high dopamine. L-Tryptophan, precursor to 5-HTP (production pathway of serotonin), when inflammation is present in the brain, feeds into the quin-olinic pathway, which is neurotoxic. It is best to first lab test whether serotonin levels are high or low, then determine if the quinolinic pathway is elevated. When Tryptophan feeds in the quinolinic path-way (neurotoxic) via interferon gamma, this stimulates astroglial cells and macrophages, and it is associated with oxidative stress.

Also, neuroinflammation on its own may induce the kynurenine pathway, which leads to the production NAD+ from the degradation of tryptophan. The kynurenine pathway has been implicated in ge-netic disorders and neurodegenerative and psychiatric disorders (depression, anxiety, and schizophrenia). Furthermore, the L-Kynurenine enzyme feeds into mTOR pathway activation.

Detox

The need to detox in today's world has become a must, as we are living in a toxic world. Detoxing resets hormones, neurotransmit-ters, and gut bacteria, reduces inflammation, and improves mood. Detoxification can be a combination of many therapeutic ap-proaches, like sauna, herbal bath, elimination diet, and intermittent fasting, with elements of relaxation through yoga, meditation, and light exercise. Research suggests heavy metal overload directly im-pacts mental health and must be reduced first before proceeding with any supplementation. I have been using herbal bath for over five years with incredible success, and I consider it one of the most effective healing therapies.

Heavy metal load of lead, mercury, aluminum, arsenic, and cad-mium have come to play a role in increasing health risk, including mental health. Sauna therapy, supporting the body in phase 1 and phase 2 detox, in conjunction with the DMSA chelation therapy un-der the proper supervision is a great way to start. A lot of patients show improvement in mental clarity after sauna therapy. Hyperther-mia has been practiced for thousands of years, and it is a very ef-fective way to detox. Hyperthermia is raising the temperature of the body above 98.5°F (through sauna). Biochemical changes take place through muscle relaxation, increased circulation, increased sweating, increased metabolism, increased pulmonary ventilation, and increased immune system function, which leads to increased detoxification.

The holistic benefits are improvements in heart and cardiovascular health, pain, joint, and muscle recovery, and pulmonary function. Hyperthermia increases the elimination of heavy metals (arsenic, mercury, lead, copper, and aluminum), mold, PCB, BPA, dioxins, phthalates, percolates, fire retardants, drugs, and organophosphates. The body needs to be prepared before and after for the increased sweating, which can cause electrolyte imbalance and dehydration. Proper hydration and supplementation with Mg, Ca, Se, Zn, and supporting detoxifiers like glutathione, alpha lipoic acid, and NAC detox is advised. During sauna therapy, great benefits for mental health are noticed with the intake of niacin, as it increases flashing through the release of histamines. Detox treatment needs to be individualized based on genetics and medical history. It is necessary to test methylation status because either hyper-methylator or hypo-methylator status will influence the response to drugs and supplements and the outcome to treatment. Niacin that increases flashing through release of histamines is directly influenced by the level of histamine in the blood.

Detoxification Support

Alpha Lipoic acid – helps the body detox of heavy metal (especially arsenic); counteracts reactive free radicals in mitochondria; and reduces glycation damage due to excess glucose in the blood.

Milk Thistle – liver detoxifier with phospholipids and flavonolignans silymarin and silybin (protect against environmental toxins and promote DNA repair).

Glutathione – the most powerful antioxidant produced in the body and the main detoxifier of the body; levels are increased by NAC (its precursor). Glutathione is a peptide consisting of three key components, the amino acids cysteine, glutamine, and lysine.

PQQ (pyrroloquinoline quinone) – activates genes that promote the formation of new mitochondria (the cell energy powerhouse);

these genes support healthy body weight and normal sugar metabolism.

Fish oil – contains EPA and DHA, essential for metabolic processes; reduces the risk of cardiovascular disease and reduces blood pressure; great benefits in reducing depression, anxiety, and cognitive decline.

Coenzyme Q10 – essential component of mitochondrial function (older population have been found to have 50% less than young adults) and very important in people after age 30. Growing scientific research links a deficiency of CoQ10 to age-related mitochondrial disorders. Very important in the detoxification process.

Resveratrol – phytoalexin and polyphenolic components. Research shows that it promotes healthy insulin, reduces inflammation, enhances mitochondrial function, protects against the effects of a high-fat diet, and aids in detoxification (mimicked many favorable gene expression changes seen in a calorie-restricted diet).

Green Tea extract – studies show it helps maintain cellular DNA and membrane structural integrity. Antioxidant contains polyphenols (catechins) and flavones, particularly EGCG (epigallocatechin gallate).

EGCG – powerful antioxidant that is 25-100 times more potent than certain vitamins; one cup of green tea provides 10-40 mg of polyphenols (more potent than broccoli, spinach, and carrots). Protects from oxidative damage due to free radicals.

NRF2 (nuclear factor erythroid 2) – helps regulate the antioxidant proteins that prevent the oxidative damage caused by inflammation. It is a transcription factor that regulates phase 2 detox and protects blood sugar balance, neurodegeneration, obesity, heavy metal detox, etc. It is increased by phytonutrients like turmeric, ginseng, ginkgo, and grape seed extract.

Circadian Rhythm

We have an internal rhythm that is regulated by the day and night cycle that activates the detoxification pathway relays on gut microbes and the rhythm of cortisol, insulin, and hormones. The circadian rhythm is synchronized with the 24 hours of the natural cycle of the Earth, and all of our body tissues express circadian genes. Chinese medicine figured this out a long time ago through the 12 meridians; each particular hour in the day corresponds to a particular organ in the system, which detoxifies and resets. There is a synchronization of cell metabolism with biological process, allowing the body to have a certain rhythm.

Circadian rhythm regulates GI function, nutrient absorption, and cell proliferation and motility. Periodic fasting has a direct effect on the gut microbiota because it resets the circadian rhythm. It is believed that circadian rhythm is originates in hypothalamus, directly above the optic nerve and directly connected with our limbic system (center of our emotions). The circadian rhythm is implicated in inflammation, hormonal dysregulation, and insulin resistance.

The night rhythm is a parasympathetic rhythm that leads to body repairs, hormones production, growth, neurotransmitter reset, and bodily healing. The limbic system becomes hypersensitive when the circadian rhythm is not synchronized. When this rhythm is off, there is sleeplessness, weight gain, mood disorders, and dis-ease. It is recommended to eat with the circadian rhythm: eat meals, no snacks, big breakfast, modest lunch, and small dinner. Adrenal fatigue occurs when the circadian rhythm is off. I usually address adrenal fatigue (and sometimes masked chronic fatigue) with glandular B1 (depleted by stress), B6, B5, and adaptogens Rhodiola, Glycyrrhiza, Ashwagandha, and Eleutherococcus in addition to DHEA (best to test levels first). Things that disturb our circadian rhythm are physical and emotional trauma, viral infection, EMF, heavy metal, and light-emitting devises (blue light). The solution to reset the circadian rhythm is get natural light (watch sunrise and sunset), sleep in complete darkness (blue light inhibits melatonin) and practice empowerment (awareness of the moment, sensation, and acceptance).

Sleep is very important because regulates aging, mood and neurodegeneration through energy metabolism, epigenetics, autophagy, and circadian rhythm pathways. Melatonin declines with aging and it is regulated by the circadian rhythm. Certain medications cause deficiency of melatonin, for example SSRIs and beta-blockers.

Melatonin was found to be pro-inflammatory through Il 17 A and Th 17 and it also has anti-inflammatory effects. For this reason, melatonin is not for everyone, especially for those with autoimmunity. Additionally, I am a big supporter of helping the body to make its own melatonin rather than supplementing it.

Circadian Rhythm Support

Centella asiatica (Gotu Kola) – asiatic acid research suggests that Centella asiatica protects from neurotoxicity. In Indian culture, it has been used for mental turbulence for all three doshas: vata, pitta, and kapha.

Holy basil – anti-anxiolytic, COX 2 inhibitor; lowers fasting and post-meal blood sugar; enhances glutathione S-transferase.

Berberine – affects dopamine and reduces glucose production in the liver; affects CYP3A4.

Phosphatidylcholine – 1,200mg with food for memory, anxiety, and brain health.

Curcumin – reduces oxidative stress and increases methylation; helps with depression, anxiety, and detoxification; is liver protective and anti-inflammatory; it clears from the body quickly and needs higher doses to have an effect.

Lithium orotate – natural alternative to lithium carbonate; needs folate supplementation for better optimization.

Vitex (chaste tree) – increases dopamine and progesterone. Progesterone has been shown to enhance restful sleep.

R-alpha-lipoic acid – part of Krebs cycle; improves mitochondrial health; fat-soluble antioxidant crosses cell membrane; helps inhibit brain degeneration.

Phosphatidylserine and phosphatidylcholine – anxiolytic; part of cell membrane; key role in cell-to-cell signaling; reduces cortisol response to stress.

Molybendum – for bipolar and sulfites-sensitive people.

L-Theanine – anti-anxiolytic; supports GABA production.

Intermittent fasting, mTOR, and Autophagy

mTOR (mechanistic target of rapamycin) is a major intracellular signaling pathway in regulating all cycles related to proliferation and longevity through apoptosis, cell growth, and protein synthesis. It serves regulation of cell metabolism, growth, proliferation, survival, phosphorylation, homeostasis of protein synthesis, transcription, autophagy, and metabolism. Too much mTOR activation contributes to cancer, depression, diabetes, neurodegeneration, and psychiatric disorders. mTOR is a component of the 3 kinase (PI3K) pathways of nutrients, cellular energy, and oxygen.

One important role of mTOR is in regulating autophagy (cleaning of the cells). It has been found that autophagy prevents neurodegeneration, autoimmunity, infection, necrosis, cancer, and infections. Autophagy is a catabolic process where normal cells digest damaged cells and recycle the nutrients.

Intermittent fasting activates autophagy, inhibits the mTOR pathway, activates AMPK, and stimulates SIRT1. SIRT1 is very important in reducing inflammation through deacetylation of transcription factors like p65 and NF-kB. Calorie restriction can extend the life span and reduces iron accumulation (iron accumulation promotes aging). Through intermittent fasting that promotes autophagy, the body resets itself. Autophagy reabsorbs dead cells and recycles them. Our cells have to die and be recycled in order for us to stay healthy; it is part of our circadian rhythm to detoxify the body. Inflammation stimulates mTOR. When eating all the time, we stimulate mTOR (signaling autophagy to shut down). Certain nutrients, like green tea extract, also mimic the effect of caloric restriction. The fasting metabolism modulates the inflammatory markers, like the interleukin-12/interleukin-10 cytokine axis. The goal of intermittent fasting is to mimic starvation and induce autophagy. Autophagy may prevent cancer, diabetes, autoimmunity, cardiomyopathy, neurodegeneration, and mental diseases. Natural plant-based compounds that induce autophagy are: apigenin, resveratrol, honokiol, curcumin, berberine, rosehip, pterostilbene, and quercetin.

Lifestyle, environmental factors, and genetics may alter mTOR and autophagy. Our genetics is what makes us, but what really breaks us is influenced by epigenetics. Epigenetics is influenced by everything we do outside of our genetic heritage, like the air we breathe, water, sunshine, emotions, thoughts, lifestyle, exercise, and nutrition. Drugs alter our gene expression and can turn genes off and on. For these reasons, the genetic test for genes/drugs interaction is a good way to start before placing anyone on an SSRI, SNRI, or any other type of drug medication. Genetic testing is very important in determining the treatment and assessing the outcome. When we see mutation (SNPs) in the pathways of neurotransmitter production, it gives us clues for how to modulate the immune system. There is a therapeutic order of treatment; certain health elements must be addressed first, and then body needs to be prepared for the next level. At the foundation of the therapeutic order of health is detoxifying the body—removing the cellular debris, cleaning up the diet, and removing toxic load. I start first with testing for gut bacteria, nutritional deficiency, level of antioxidants and detoxifiers in the body, neurotransmitter levels, and genetics. Only after a full assessment, I nourish and correct deficiencies through nutrition and supplementation.

Autophagy Support

Berberine – reduces tumor growth in vivo; it can be found in goldenseal, oregano, grapes, and barberries. Berberine inhibits the electron transport chain in mitochondria causing, a change in the AMP/ATP ratio, which in turn activates AMPK, which inhibits mTOR.
Glutathione – modulates starvation-induced autophagy.

Resveratrol – rich in polyphenols; induces autophagy by directly inhibiting mTOR-ULK1 pathway.

Curcumin – inflammation research suggests that it supports autophagia, inhibits mTOR, and has an anti-inflammatory effect.

Niacinamide – induces autophagy through activation of SIRT 1.

Rosehip – activates AMPK by phosphorylation inhibits mTOR.

Neurosupport and Neuroprotect

Apigenin – found in olive oil, sage, oregano, rosemary, onion, and peppermint.

Mucuna pruriens – mood enhancement and mental focus (dopamine booster).

Aceyl-L-Carnitine – in 2,000-2,500mg is particularly good for rebuilding the memory, increasing the connection between neurons.

Pycnogenol – more and more studies suggest it is neuroprotective, helping with oxidative damage of the brain, skin aging, and metabolic syndrome.

Lactobacillus heveticus and Bifidobacterium longus – these two probiotics have been found to support help with depression and anxiety (30 days).

Lactoferricin – scavenges excess iron to prevent free radical damage; beneficial for bacteria growth; modulates the immune system.

DMAE (dimethylaminoethanol) – precursor to acetylcholine (naturally found in sardine & anchovies); use to support anxiety, dementia, ADD/ADHD, learning, and motivation.

Adaptogen plants – help the body fight stress and better cope with anxiety; aid in sleep because they regulate the cortisol levels. Examples: ashwagandha, rhodiola, cordyceps, and lemon balm.

Ashwagandha has been found to inhibit the enzyme that degrades acetylcholine in the aging brain.

Turmeric – natural anti-inflammatory; extremely beneficial for mental health; research studies show improvements in depression and anxiety.

Glycine – improves memory, attention, REM, and bipolar.

SAMUEL LEE, M.D.

Inositol (vitamin B8) – supports GABA pathway; used in nutritional approach for OCD, bipolar, panic, depression, and PCOS.

Zinc – is a component of 200 enzymes, and its deficiency associated with depression, anxiety, and neurodegenerative disorders. Zn is needed for synthesis of dopamine and GABA. Zn deficiency causes copper overload and alters GABA. Excessive Zn may produce anemia due to the effect on reduction in iron stores.

Copper – inhibits three enzymes in the glycolytic pathway in the first phase of carbohydrate metabolism, resulting in reduced ATP production, which translates into fatigue. It has been said that copper pushes dopamine into the norepinephrine fight-or-flight pathway.

Niacinamide – inhibits sirtuins (class of protein that remove acetyl groups from histones) and promotes methylation.

NRF2 – plays a role in three critical antioxidants in the body: glutathione, superoxide dismutase, and catalase. It is a transcription factor that regulates expression of phase 2 detox and it is expressed in every tissue of the body, with prevalence in liver and kidneys. It interacts with tumor suppressor protein (P53) and nuclear factor kappa-beta (NF-KB).

SAMe – the methylating agent for serotonin, melatonin, norepinephrine, dopamine, DNA/RNA, phospholipids, protein, and creatine. It helps produce and degrades the neurotransmitters. Insufficient production of SAMe hinders methylation. Methylation continuously repairs the DNA. SAMe can be low due to B12 deficiency, malabsorption, toxins, or polymorphism. SAMe works on three pathways: methylation (repairs DNA), transulfuration (synthesis of cysteine and glutathione), and aminopropylation. SAMe helps produce and degrade the neurotransmitters. Before supplementation, levels of SAMe need to be tested first. SAMe acts as natural reuptake inhibitor for serotonin, dopamine, and norepinephrine.

Glutathione – produced and used by the liver to detox many substances including formaldehyde, acetaminophen, drugs, and benzopyrene. Every year, the level of glutathione in the body drops by 1%. It is made out of glutamate, cysteine, and glycine. Low glutathione tends to cause hypomethylation.

168

Ganoderma Lucidum – triterpene-rich extract, which great for anxiety and Alzheimer's; 3g/day. It has been shown to help balance the immune system away from a Th2 dominant, reducing pro-inflammatory cytokines and reducing depression. It has been found to inhibit histamine release; it is anti-inflammatory, antioxidant, and anti-microbial; aids in immune modulation, inducing apoptosis, and is anti-hypertensive.

Hericium erinaceous – stimulates the production of nerve growth factor and promotes the repair and regeneration of neurons; shows improvement in anxiety and Alzheimer's; 3-5g/day.

About the Author

Dr. Ellie Wright NMD, MA, CHT has been an avid international medical researcher and presenter for EGW Research Institute LLC. She graduated from an accredited Naturopathic Medical school (SCNM, USA) with a doctoral degree in naturopathic medicine and she is licensed to practice medicine in Arizona as naturopathic physician. Her background also includes a graduate certificate in Geriatrics & Gerontology and a master's degree. In her private practice, Magnolia Personalized Medicine (USA), she focuses on the holistic aspects of health, incorporating botanical medicine, acupuncture, orthomolecular therapy, personalized nutrition, homeopathy, and mind/body therapy. She is licensed to prescribed both drugs and plant-based medicine, understanding and utilizing the best of both worlds.

To learn more, please visit Dr. Wright's website: www.magnoliapersonalizedmedicine.com.

CHAPTER 15:
CONCLUSION

A. All Mental Health Conditions Are a Lesson, a Blessing, and an Opportunity for Growth and Experience

In most spiritual traditions, suffering can be seen as a doorway into awakening. All mental health "diagnoses" can be viewed as opportunities. He who is "forgiven much can love much." He who has experienced the darkest of days can appreciate the light all the more. And he who perseveres and overcomes mental health problems now has the moral authority and consciousness to talk about it from his heart and help people who are going through similar trials. And service is the culmination of all spiritual practice. When we go through trials and tribulations and overcome, it gives us the ability to serve other people from our hearts who may be struggling from a similar condition.

Mental health conditions result from an imbalance in belief systems, leading to conditioned/programmed thoughts, which lead to low-vibration emotions, which leads to the expression of genes, proteins, and hormones that are in alignment with the belief systems. These belief systems can be passed on from generation to generation, society to society, or adopted during childhood or even adulthood. Once these belief systems have been reconditioned and reprogrammed into ones that promote vitality and health, the brain's natural pharmacy will start to produce natural dopamine, serotonin, endorphins, etc., in a balanced manner that will activate each human being's birthright, which is freedom, joy, and bliss.

These belief systems, however, need to be brought to aware-ness, reconditioned, and reprogrammed to be in alignment with the person's true nature. Eventually, one can reach a point where they let go of all belief systems and have complete trust and surrender in the present moment and in the inherent goodness of the Uni-verse. A good question to ask is: when human beings are stripped of all conditioning and programming, are they inherently "good"? I choose to believe that the answer to this question is yes. If not, then we are all in trouble. The good news is that the collective conscious-ness, nature, and the Universe are working for us not against us. This means that each mental health "condition" that comes to sur-face is brought up so that it can be integrated; so that one can awaken and help other people who are suffering from the same type of discomfort. One must remember that the greatest souls on the planet are those who have overcome a tremendous amount of suf-fering, learned from it, and have helped others obtain new heights in consciousness. All of the resources, ideas, and technology that are needed to help save Mother Earth from destruction are already here. There is abundance everywhere, starting with an abundance of prana. All that is needed is a rise in collective consciousness, which is now happening. It is an exciting time to be alive, and if you are reading this sentence, you are a part of an exciting movement that is seeking to reintegrate Ourselves back into wholeness so that we can help others and Mother Earth back into wholeness as well.

The only difference between "holy men" of the past and us is that they had been able to fully deprogram all societal and intergen-erational conditioning and trauma so that they could fully be present and completely merge with their Higher Selves and become One with infinite substance, or All that is. In this natural state, we will see that the mind is empty, present, and in a state of natural bliss; We are not worried about the past or the future but simply grateful to be alive in this present moment where all of time (eternity) is happen-ing.

B. How to Pull the Mind out of the Body

The following was inspired by Chapter 5 in Dr. Joe Dispenza's book, *Becoming Supernatural.* In this chapter, Dr. Dispenza beautifully describes the process of accessing our body's own innate energy and then learning how to move or transmute the energy. Science is slowly starting to understand that each energy center in the body has its own "brain." Each chakra or energy center is connected with its own unique nervous system and has a "mind of its own." All of these systems are connected back to the spine, which connects these communication systems back to the brain.

The first three energy centers are located in the "physical" plane. These energy centers are associated with our human instinct for survival. Each energy center has corresponding emotions. The first energy center, or the first chakra, has to do with lust, wanting to be seen as sexually desirable by others, etc. Guilt, sadness, fear, depression, shame, unworthiness, and low self-esteem are associated with the second energy center. Problems with anger, frustration, control issues, and self-importance are emotions associated with the third energy center. Please note, however, that these are only the low-vibratory emotions associated with these centers. When properly integrated, these survival emotions can be transmuted into positive emotions, such as grounded creativity. Please note that it is possible to move these energies up the spine, and as the energy moves up the spine, it will evolve, or transmute, into higher vibration energy. The energy will become less dense. This does not mean that "sex is bad" or that the physical/survival energy centers are bad. It simply means that we can learn how to balance these centers and learn how to transmute the energy in the lower centers so that we can use the energy to create and love with.

Dr. Dispenza reports that we can use the power of the breath to liberate the lower center energies and transmute them to experience higher vibration emotions, have mystical experiences, and turn the survival emotions into creative emotions.

Ancient sciences call this art the "raising of the kundalini." Dr. Dispenza explains that the body is like a magnet. Just as there is a north and south pole on the earth there is also a north and south pole of the spine. The brain is the north pole, and the bottom of the spine or sacrum is the south pole. The flow of energy through the chakras, or energy centers, creates an electromagnetic field, which envelopes each person. However, when one is in "survival mode," energy is being pulled from the first three energy centers, it does not flow throughout the body, and the electromagnetic field becomes "stuck."

Dr. Dispenza explains that the breath is the key to keep the energies moving throughout the energy centers. With each inhale there is a subtle movement of the sacrum forward, and the cerebrospinal fluid is pushed up the spine to the base of the brain. Dr. Dispenza next explains that as we breathe and squeeze or contract the pelvic muscles (root lock) as well as the lower and upper abdominal muscles, the energy from the lower energy centers is pumped up the spine to the higher energy centers. Please understand that where one focuses their attention is where the energy flows. Thus, as one engages root lock (squeezes the sex muscles as one does when urinating) and squeezes the abdominal muscles and focuses on the third eye or pineal gland, the energy flows up the spine to the point of attention. Thus, the energies of the first three energy centers are transmuted up into the energy center located between the eyebrows, also known as the third or first eye. At the top of the breath, one can hold it, keep squeezing, and further bring the energy into the creative center of the brain.

Dr. Dispenza explains that the cerebral spinal fluid is made up of proteins, salts, and solution. As the proteins and salts dissolve, they become charged, thus creating an "induction field." An invisible field of electromagnetic energy moving in the direction of the charge thus pulls energy up from the first three energy centers up to the brain. This creates a field of electromagnetic energy around the body and creates a torus field, just like the one around the earth. If this practice is done consistently and correctly, it will awaken "a sleeping dragon." The process of raising this energy is seldom discussed in modern literature, as it is a mysterious energy that will awaken you to the hidden truths of the Universe, help you remember who you really are, and give you a renewed purpose for your incarnation. The way this happens is unique to each individual. The Universe will become alive to the one who raises the energy with pure intention and consistent practice.

As the energy from the lower centers is pulled up the spine, it enters the "thalamic gait," and all the energy is permitted to enter into the brain. The energy flows up the pranic tube (shushumna) in the spine, to the back of the brain stem. The reticular formation (a cluster of nuclei) activates the lower parts of the brain so that the energy can then flow through the brain to the thalamus (midbrain/relay center), then to the neocortex (higher brain center). From the thalamus the energy also flows to the pineal gland, which releases powerful elixirs that quiet the analytical, or thinking, brain! Dr. Dispenza calls this "like an orgasm in your head." When the energy reaches the neocortex, the brain starts producing gamma brain waves. Dr. Dispenza calls these "supernatural brain waves." The brain waves come from the inner energy centers, producing a heightened sense of consciousness, which can be experienced in many mystical ways. This also produces more brain coherence. Therefore, the brain is now using the most powerful creative energy in the world (sexual energy, the energy used to create life) and transmuting this energy to be put to use to creating from the higher emotional frequencies. Dr. Dispenza also describes a "prana tube" in the spine, which this life force energy travels through to get to the brain. Moving this energy up the spine takes intention and will. Thus, the emotions of guilt, shame, and fear can be transmuted into joy, love, peace, compassion, and empowerment.

Please understand that the raising of this energy in ancient traditions is considered a sacred practice. The energy can only flow through energy centers, which are open. It is very important that the heart energy center or intention be in the correct space when this practice is engaged or else the energy can become stuck. One could compare the raising of this energy as pure white energy.

When one is not ready to raise this energy and engage in the practice, sometimes the body of pain can be activated, and this pure white energy will mix with the not-so-clear energy of the different energy centers. This can lead to symptoms that can mimic psychosis, anxiety, paranoia, and depression. In fact, I believe many psychiatrists often misdiagnose the raising of this energy with the diagnosis of schizophrenia. Therefore, it is important to engage this practice with good intentions, an open heart, and a desire to know the truth of the Universe. And the truth shall set you free.

C. For the Advanced Spiritual Seeker Who Desires Rapid Self-Realization

Please realize there are many ways to completely merge with your Higher Self or God. The mantric way is a sure way to merge with the divine. Yoga and meditation may take you to the door of God, but the right mantras, with the right intentions, will take you to God then merge you with God. Scripture says, "In the beginning was the Word, and the Word was with God, and the Word was God..." Everything started with sound. The Word binds God because all prana originated from the Word. Many of these mantras were divinely inspired from Source/God/Creator and given to "holy men" of old who would go out into nature and meditate for days and receive these mantras. These mantras have helped many completely merge with infinity and have endured for a time such as this. In the Aquarian age we find ourselves in, sound is and will be the future of medicine.

On a purely physical level, the vibrating of mantras will stimulate the tip of the tongue to the 84 pressure points on the upper palate, thereby stimulating the pituitary and pineal glands to bring the entire glandular system into coherence. When mantras are created so that there is only four to six breaths/minute, it will also activate the parasympathetic nervous system and bring the body into a state of divine peace.

On a mental level, mantras are the quickest way to quiet an overactive mind. Almost every person who walks into a psychiatrist's office has an overactive mind, which is spewing out negativity that has been programmed and conditioned. When people believe these thoughts, it leads to low-vibration emotions, which leads to the genetic expression of DNA, proteins, hormones, etc., which are in coherence with the vibration of the emotions one consistently vibrates. The mantras, when chanted with positive intention from the heart, will not only quiet the mind but will clear out the subconscious mind from its negative programming. By the law of osmosis, we understand that we become the energy that we continually speak and surround ourselves with. When we chant and meditate on ancient mantras packed with truth, we began the sure process of merging with God and our Higher Selves. It will not only clean out our subconscious minds of all negativity but will reprogram the subconscious mind to the Universal truths contained within these mantras. One way to look at these mantras is that they are neuro-somatic codes of light that penetrate the denser areas of the body. They then bring awareness to the physical, mental, and spiritual parts of our Selves that want to be absorbed into the "light." The mantras, when vibrated with pure intent, will bring loving awareness to the parts of the Self that need reintegration. As more and more light is brought to the subtle body, eventually, the heart will become soft and open. Once the heart is open, life becomes easy.

On an energetic level, please know that sound is the mother of light. Sound becomes light. And God said, "Let there be light, and there was light..." When these mantras are chanted from the heart with love, it will lift you to the higher dimensions where you will begin to access your birthright of love, freedom, truth, and joy. As you chant these ancient sounds packed with truth, the sound vibrations are guaranteed to become light and activate your light body until you are completely merged back into Source from which you came. Mystical experiences will occur in your daily life until your whole life will become a living synchronicity and love story with the Universe. However, don't take my word for it. Ignorance is dismissing something before even trying it. Test the process for a month and see if anything changes. The mantric way is a guaranteed way to help achieve Self-realization and ultimately Self-actualization. It has worked for many people before you and will work for you if practiced with sincerity and consistency.

Self-realization is the greatest gift you can give to the world. Raising the kundalini energy at the base of the spine is the surest and quickest way to obtain Self-realization. In the process of Self-realization, you will experience the following steps in no particular order: a realization that everything is connected, you are an Infinite Being, and the Soul never dies. From there, as you realize your Infinite soul, you will face the greatest battle ever fought—with your own ego/your lower self. Through your spiritual practices, you will be able to integrate the lower self and connect consistently with the Higher Self. From there, you will have an epiphanic awakening that not only is everything connected but that God/the Universal Force is within you. Then, after the ego is not killed but incorporated as your servant, you will find a unique purpose/mission, which will somehow involve using your creative abilities to serve others and make this world a better place. Then the Self-actualization will occur, where limiting beliefs/karma/the desire for money/fame etc., is put aside for the sake of selfless service/love as One realizes God is in everything and everyone and we are all connected. Then the beautiful part of selfless service begins...and never ends. And when the ego pipes up, you notice it, send it love, and go back to your practices, keep expanding, keep growing, keep creating, and keep serving. Keep bringing in the light, day by day, into the mind, heart, and body until every cell vibrates at the frequency of the light/emotions/vibrations you are bringing in. Some call this ascension. Then spiritual practice becomes everything you do and who you are. Then, at the end, you can choose to forget it all and repeat the cycle again, all for the sake of the God/Source within wanting to experience oneself through Self and through "others."

Health is vibration. The advanced spiritual/conscious seeker can turn to practices such as kundalini yoga. In my personal journey I have been blessed to meet and study under a spiritual master, Dr. Joseph Michael Levy. He has created a spiritual tool called Naam Yoga, which is a powerful tool to help the seeker realize and merge with their higher Self. It is what I like to call "kundalini yoga on crack." Naam is a combination of ancient mantras, kundalini yoga, music, and breathwork.

Naam (which means "the Word") is the quickest and surest way that I've found to obtain complete Self-realization. "In the beginning was the Word, and the Word was with God, and the Word was God…"(John 1:1). Health is vibration. Naam is sacred vibration. It all started with the vibration of sound, sometimes referred to as the Word "Om." If you go back to the Word, you go back to the begin- ning; therefore, you can cure all things that come after. As you chant the Word, you start merging with the vibration, which is a high-fre- quency vibration, which will start to bring awareness to all distor- tions in thought and squeeze out any falsely held beliefs that are not in alignment with the primal Source. Instead of treating the result of falsely held beliefs, which produce symptoms, why not go back to the beginning and merge with the primal Source from which we all come? The mechanism of how it works is a divine mystery, but I AM a witness that it is a sure way of achieving Self-realization. Not only is it working for me, but it has worked for thousands of people who have come before. It is an ancient tradition that works. What- ever tool one uses, the tool should never point you towards an ex- ternal act, person, or methodology but always point you back to your own heart/Higher Self where all answers lie. Naam is simply a powerful tool that helps you connect with your divinity within.

Before I found this powerful spiritual tool, I was obsessed with finding different modalities to evolve consciousness. I was traveling the world, going to seminars, reading books, and listening to nu- merous podcasts, searching for the best, most rapid way to merge with my Higher Self. After I found Naam, I quit searching. I won't lie; the following two years after I found this tool were intense, magical, and sometimes difficult. What I experienced is unexplainable in words. It was an awakening to the beauty of the Universe but also the "darkness" within me. As my darkness was brought to light and I realized that the "darkness" in the world is merely a reflection of myself, I became emerged into a deep journey into surrender, hon- esty, and vulnerability. This practice is not for everyone. However, for the conscious seeker who desires "enlightenment" and to know who they really are more than anything else, this practice can offer rapid Self-realization. However, before attempting this practice one needs to be in a sincere state of desirelessness with a firm intention to only do the will of God. If this is practiced with selfish motives, or a desire of power, it can precipitate a difficult spiritual experience of purification.

For those who want to rapidly Self-realize and merge with the divine, I have created a program that will help you in this process. Please do not start this practice if you do not want change in your life. The vibration and energy created by this practice is guaranteed to squeeze out the conditioning and programming in the subconscious mind and produce effective change towards spiritual, emotional, and mental health. The seeker may also experience profound mystical experiences in the process, which are simply experiences the Universe gives the seeker so that they can remember who they are and use these experiences as inspiration for service. However, please be advised that between the crucifixion and resurrection there were three days spent in the tomb. This means that in this process, there will be a period of clearing, seeking, and merging. This process requires discipline and strong willpower towards the desired goal—to be free of programming and manifest the highest destiny for all sentient beings during this lifetime. Please practice with sincerity, from the heart, and with a loving intention, and this powerful spiritual tool will help you find your Truth. And the Truth will set you free. This practice is a calling for the advanced conscious seeker only, and one should search his or her heart to see if this is the right time for this practice.

Holy men of the past would spend days meditating and connecting with the unseen world and receive these mantras. They would often times come back with alchemical sounds, vibrations, and formulas. These mantras, when combined with breathwork, movement, and loving intention produce a guaranteed and mysterious formula, which helps all seekers reach their highest conscious potential. This practice will not only change your life but your destiny. The vibration and energy created from these practices on a physical level will start to vibrate the cells at a divine frequency. **This will lead to a natural release of addictions and habits that no longer serve the physical body.** On an emotional/mental level, these mantras are **the quickest way to quiet an overactive mind.** They will also slow the rate of the breath down to three to six breaths per minute, which will naturally activate the parasympathetic nervous system and produce brain waves that will enable you to receive the bandwidth/downloads from the Universe. It is fairly common to receive divine inspiration and ideas while chanting. On a divine plane, these mantras will connect you with the unseen world and help you quickly manifest the loving intentions and goals that you desire to obtain.

These advanced methods have been hidden from the public for a good reason. They are powerful and they work. However, at the appropriate time, they are being revealed to those seekers who are ready to merge with the vibration of the Divine. Please practice with a loving intention for the liberation of all sentient beings.

I have prayerfully formulated a morning practice using the formulas of Naam, sacred music, and kundalini yoga for the seeker who is ready to take their consciousness to the next level and fully remember who they are and for what reason they incarnated. These practices were inspired from my dear teacher Dr. Joseph Michael Levry, who gave me my first practice and inspired me through divine unconditional love, support, and faith. When I first received these practices, I was a practicing westernized physician working at Kaiser Permanente. Within the first year, I was having mystical experiences. I followed my heart, quit my job, and went on an all-out journey into exploring all things related to consciousness. By the second year, my heart had melted, and all of my desires were being melted into how I could use my creative gifts to help others. This whole process was highly experiential. If you do these practices consistently for 30 days, there is likely to be a cosmic shift in your vibration, your life, and eventually your destiny. I can honestly say these practices changed my destiny. And for that I am eternally grateful and would like to humbly offer them as an option for you.

This program has been prayerfully and includes a written tutorial of an hour-long morning practice, which incorporates elements of kundalini yoga, breathwork, and ancient mantras. You will also receive a link to a video where I explain and demonstrate this practice. If you are interested in rapid Self-realization, please visit this website: 21days.thespiritualpsychiatrist.com.

D. My Vision

Someone recently asked me, "What is your vision for the future of mental health?"

This was my reply:

"My vision for the future of mental health is to create consciousness-based treatment centers around the world that combine ancient Eastern modalities with the latest Western technologies. Residents who are magnetized to the centers will fly in from around the world and will receive customized treatment protocols that provide the physical, mental, and subtle energetic bodies with the ideal environment to rapidly integrate itself back into wholeness. Once the physical body is stabilized and integrated, consciousness-raising technologies that already exist will be utilized to help each resident obtain rapid Self-realization, discover their divine purpose/blueprint, and then feel empowered with the right tools and support to use their creative gifts to help raise global consciousness.

The first integrative center will began with a group of conscious "healers" who have a common intention of opening as many hearts as possible during this lifetime and who have learned to love each other unconditionally through practical exercises that draw upon vulnerability, impartiality (non-judgment), empathy, and curious wonder towards one another.

Once the integrative "healers" have done the work and accepted and integrated themselves into one group consciousness, they will powerfully work together as one to harmonize their talents and creative abilities to change the paradigm of mental health globally. This process will happen naturally, with grace, ease, and childlike joy, as the power of love radiating from their open hearts will magnetize the right land, funding, and beings at exactly the right time through the law of attraction. Once the first center is started and successful, it will naturally divide and spread at exactly the right moment in coherence with the plans and laws of the Universe.

We already have all of the technologies and resources needed to save Mother Earth. All we need is to raise global consciousness one resident at a time. In this process, the outdated, westernized, capitalistic, hierarchal system of mental health treatment, which includes labels, diagnoses, and symptom-focused management will naturally disintegrate as consciousness rises and the Truth is unfolded. And now I realize: the future is now. This process has already begun and is now happening. It is an exciting time to be alive, and I AM grateful to all who have contributed, who are contributing, and who will contribute to complete this vision."

Dr. Lee has created a non-profit organization called Free to Rise to bring this vision to reality in the near future. If you or your loved one has received positive energy from this book, please feel free to follow your intuition, and bless this vision into reality. You can donate at www.patreon.com/spiritualpsychiatry/creators. Please only give if it's from your heart! Thank you.

For those who would like to connect with Dr. Lee please check out his website at: www.TheSpiritualPsychiatrist.com or send him an email at: SamuelbsleeMD@gmail.com

For those who would like to get in touch with the author, Dr. Samuel Lee, and/or see him for a one-on-one session, please visit his website at: www.TheSpiritualPsychiatrist.com.

ACKNOWLEDGMENTS

I would like to acknowledge….

My dearest Mother, Byung Sook Lee. Thank you for praying for your son ceaselessly. Thank you for preparing your sacred womb so that I could choose it. Thank you for being a divine reflection of what it means to be a true lover and follower of Jesus. I am alive today because of your prayers and would choose your sacred womb every single time. I love you.

Zora Knauf. Thank you for being the best editor. Thank you for helping out in the creative process of this book and arranging my words so that they make sense. Your expertise is priceless.

Naomi Rose. Thank you for following your intuition and for the creative, conscious energy put into the design of the cover of this book. Your Spirit is a gift.

Michael Estrella. Thank you and your team for the amazing video production and for being a friend.

Bibliography

Bredesen, D. (2017). *The End of Alzheimer's: The First Program to Prevent and Reverse Cognitive Decline.* New York: Penguin Random House LLC.

Brod, S., Rattazzi, L., Piras, G., & D'Acquisto, F. (2014). 'As above, so below' examining the interplay between emotion and the immune system. *Immunology*, 311–318.

Buhner, S. H. (2004). *The Secret Teachings of Plants: The Intelligence of the Heart in the Direct Perception of Nature.* Rochester: Bear & Company.

Cao, L., Liu, C., Wang, F., & Wang, H. (2013). SIRT1 negatively regulates amyloid-beta-induced inflammation via the NF-κB pathway. *Brazilian Journal of Medical and Biological Research*, 659–669.

Chen, X., Chen, C., Fan, S., Wu, S., Yang, F., Fang, Z., . . . Li, Y. (2018). Omega-3 polyunsaturated fatty acid attenuates the inflammatory response by modulating microglia polarization through SIRT1-mediated deacetylation of the HMGB1/NF-κB pathway following experimental tr2018aumatic brain injury. *Journal of Neuroinflammation*, 116.

Cheng, S., Li, S., & Leung, P. (2019). Fibroblast Growth Factor 21 Stimulates Pancreatic Islet Autophagy via Inhibition of AMPK-mTOR Signaling. *International Journal of Molecular Sciences*, E2517.

Chiu, C., Chyau, C., Chen, C., Lee, L., Chen, W., Liu, J., . . . Mong, M. (2018). Erinacine A-Enriched Hericium erinaceus Mycelium Produces Antidepressant-Like Effects through

Modulating BDNF/PI3K/Akt/GSK-3β Signaling in Mice. *International Journal of Molecular Sciences*, 341.

Chiu, C., Chyau, C., Chen, C., Lee, L., Chen, W., Liu, J., . . . Mong, M. (2018). Erinacine A-Enriched Hericium erinaceus Mycelium Produces Antidepressant-Like Effects through Modulating BDNF/PI3K/Akt/GSK-3β Signaling in Mice. *International Journal of Molecular Sciences*, 341.

Crane, K. (2014, August 27). *Why You Should Consider a High Prana Diet*. Retrieved from U.S. News & World Report: https://health.usnews.com/health-news/health-wellness/articles/2014/08/27/why-you-should-consider-a-high-prana-diet

D'Acquisto, F. (2017). Affective immunology: where emotions and the immune response converge. *Dialogues in Clinical Neuroscience*, 9-19.

Dean Ornish, M. (n.d.). *Nutrition*. Retrieved from Ornish Lifestyle Medicine: https://www.ornish.com/proven-program/nutrition/

Desideri, E., Filomeni, G., & Ciriolo, M. R. (2012). Glutathione participates in the modulation of starvation-induced autophagy in carcinoma cells. *Autophagy*, 1769–1781.

Desideri, E., Filomeni, G., & Ciriolo, M. R. (2012). Glutathione participates in the modulation of starvation-induced autophagy in carcinoma cells. *Autophagy*, 1769-1781.

Diagnostic and Statistical Manual of Mental Disorders, Fifth Edition. (2013). Arlington: American Psychiatric Association.

Dispenza, J. (2017). *Becoming Supernatural: How Common People Are Doing the Uncommon*. Carlsbad: Hay House Inc.

Dossey, L. (2013). *One Mind: How Our Individual Mind Is Part of a Greater Consciousness and Why It Matters*. Carlsbad: Hay House Inc.

Emoto, M. (2005). *The Hidden Messages in Water*. Hillsboro: Beyond Words Publishing Inc.

Fan, X., Wang, J., Hou, J., Lin, C., Bensoussan, A., Chang, D., . . . Wang, B. (2015). Berberine alleviates ox-LDL induced inflammatory factors by up-regulation of autophagy via AMPK/mTOR signaling pathway. *Journal of Translational Medicine*, 92.

Fan, X., Wang, J., Hou, J., Lin, C., Bensoussan, A., Chang, D., . . . Wang, B. (2015). Berberine alleviates ox-LDL induced inflammatory factors by up-regulation of autophagy via AMPK/mTOR signaling pathway. *Journal of Translational Medicine*.

Felger, J. (2017). The Role of Dopamine in Inflammation-Associated Depression: Mechanisms and Therapeutic Implications. *Current Topics in Behavioral Neurosciences*, 199-219.

Gaby, A. (2011). *Nutritional Medicine.*

Gantz, S. C., Levitt, E. S., Llamosas, N., Neve, K. A., & Williams, J. T. (2015). Depression of serotonin synaptic transmission by the dopamine precursor L-DOPA. *Cell Reports*, 944–954.

Griffiths, R. R., Johnson, M. W., Carducci, M. A., Umbricht, A., Richards, B. D., Cosimano, M. P., & Klinedinst, M. A. (2016). Psilocybin produces substantial and sustained decreases in depression and anxiety in patients with life-threatening cancer: A randomized double-blind trial. *Journal of Psychopharmachology*, 1181–1197.

Griffiths, R. R., Johnson, M. W., Carducci, M. A., Umbricht, A., Richards, W. A., Richards, B. D., . . . Klinedinst, M. A. (2016). Psilocybin produces substantial and sustained decreases in depression and anxiety in patients with life-threatening cancer: A randomized double-blind trial. *Journal of Psychopharmacology*, 1181-1197.

Hardeland, R. (2019). Aging, Melatonin, and the Pro- and Anti-Inflammatory Networks. *International Journal of Molecular Sciences*, 1223.

Hardeland, R. (2019). Aging, Melatonin, and the Pro- and Anti-Inflammatory Networks. *International Journal of Molecular Sciences*, 1223.

Innes, K. E., Selfe, T. K., Khalsa, D. S., & Kandati, S. (2016). Effects of Meditation versus Music Listening on Perceived Stress, Mood, Sleep, and Quality of Life in Adults with Early Memory Loss: A Pilot Randomized Controlled Trial. *Journal of Alzheimer's Disease*, 1277-1298.

Jamshed, H., Beyl, R., Della Manna, D., Yang, E., Ravussin, E., & Peterson, C. (2019). Early Time-Restricted Feeding Improves 24-Hour Glucose Levels and Affects Markers of the Circadian Clock, Aging, and Autophagy in Humans. *Nutrients*, E1234.

Jenwitheesuk, A., Nopparat, C., Mukda, S., Wongchitrat, P., & Govitrapong, P. (2014). Melatonin Regulates Aging and Neurodegeneration through Energy Metabolism, Epigenetics, Autophagy and Circadian Rhythm Pathways. *International Journal of Molecular Sciences*, 16848-16884.

Johnson, M. W., Garcia-Romeu, A., Cosimano, M. P., & Griffiths, R. R. (2014, September 14). *'Magic Mushrooms' Can Help Smokers Break the Habit*. Retrieved from Johns Hopkins Medicine: https://www.hopkinsmedicine.org/news/stories/mushrooms_quit_smoking.html

Kennedy, D. O. (2019). Phytochemicals for Improving Aspects of Cognitive Function and Psychological State Potentially Relevant to Sports Performance. *Sports Medicine*, 39–58.

Kim, H., Moon, J. Y., Ahn, K. S., & Cho, S. K. (2013). Quercetin Induces Mitochondrial Mediated Apoptosis and Protective Autophagy in Human Glioblastoma U373MG Cells. *Oxidative Medicine and Cellular Longevity*.

Kovarik, J. J., Kernbauer, E., Hölzl, M. A., Hofer, J., Gualdoni, G. A., Schmetterer, K. G., . . . Ohradanova-Repic, A. (2017). Fasting metabolism modulates the interleukin-12/interleukin-10 cytokine axis. *PLOS One*.

Levry, J. M. (2007). *Lifting the Veil: The Divine Code: Practical Kabbalas with Kundalini Yoga.* Rootlight Inc.

Lin, C., Kuo, Y., Chen, T., & Chien, C. (2016). Quercetin-Rich Guava (Psidium guajava) Juice in Combination with Trehalose Reduces Autophagy, Apoptosis and Pyroptosis Formation in the Kidney and Pancreas of Type II Diabetic Rats. *Molecules*, 334.

Lin, S., Fu, Y. T., Cheng, H., & Weng, C. (2017). Natural Compounds from Herbs that can Potentially Execute as Autophagy Inducers for Cancer Therapy. *International Journal of Molecular Sciences*, 1412.

Lin, S., Fu, Y., Tsai, M., Cheng, H., & Weng, C. (2017). Natural Compounds from Herbs that can Potentially Execute as Autophagy Inducers for Cancer Therapy. *International Journal of Molecular Sciences*, 1412.

Lipton, B. (2019). *Other Resouces.* Retrieved from Bruce Lipton: https://www.brucelipton.com/other-resources#belief-change

Lipton, B. H. (2019, April 10). *Dr. Bruce H. Lipton Explains How To Reprogram The Subconscious Mind.* Retrieved from YouTube.com: https://www.youtube.com/watch?v=liEPFoj4qfw

Ma, D., Li, S., Molusky, M. M., & Lin, J. D. (2012). Circadian autophagy rhythm: a link between clock and metabolism? *Trends in Endocrinology and Metabolism*, 319–325.

Malandra, O. (2011). *First Ever Human Trial Finds Magic Mushrooms Beat Severe Depression.* https://reset.me.

Maté, G. (2018). *In the Realm of Hungry Ghosts.* Bettendorf: Vermilion.

Matsuzaki, H., Shimizu, Y., Iwata, N., Kamiuchi, S., Suzuki, F., Iizuka, H., . . . Okazaki, M. (2013). Antidepressant-like effects of a water-soluble extract from the culture medium of Ganoderma lucidum mycelia in rats. *BMC Complementary and Alternative Medicine*, 370.

Matsuzaki, H., Shimizu, Y., Iwata, N., Kamiuchi, S., Suzuki, F., Iizuka, H., . . . Okazaki, M. (2013). Antidepressant-like effects of a water-soluble extract from the culture medium of Ganoderma lucidum mycelia in rats. *BMC Complementary and Alternative Medicine*, 370.

Mitchell, L. (n.d.). *The Yogic Diet: 10 Foods to Enjoy & Avoid*. Retrieved from Mindbodygreen: https://www.mindbodygreen.com/0-5870/The-Yogic-Diet-10-Foods-to-Enjoy-Avoid.html

Mittal, R., Debs, L. H., Patel, A. P., Nguyen, D., Patel, K., O'Connor, G., . . . Liu, X. Z. (2017). Neurotransmitters: The critical modulators regulating gut-brain axis. *Journal of Cellular Physiology*, 2359–2372.

Moorjani, A. (2012). *Dying to Be Me: My Journey from Cancer to Near Death to True Healing*. Carlsbad: Hay House Inc.

Newstart Lifestyle Program. (2019). Retrieved from https://www.newstart.com/

Shen, C., Dou, X., Ma, Y., Ma, W., Li, S., & Song, Z. (2017). Nicotinamide protects hepatocytes against palmitate-induced lipotoxicity via SIRT1-dependent autophagy induction. *Nutrition Research*, 40-47.

Shen, C., Dou, X., Ma, Y., Ma, W., Songtao, L., & Song, Z. (2017). Nicotinamide protects hepatocytes against palmitate-induced lipotoxicity via SIRT1-dependent autophagy induction. *Nutrition Research*.

Shi, Y., Dong, J.-W., Zhao, J.-H., Tang, L.-N., & Zhanga, J.-J. (2014). Herbal Insomnia Medications that Target GABAergic Systems: A Review of the Psychopharmacological Evidence. *Current Neuropharmacology*, 289–302.

Singer, M. A. (2007). *The Untethered Soul: The Journey Beyond Yourself*. Oakland: New Harbinger Publications, Inc.

Stone, M. (n.d.). *How to Do Holotropic Breathwork*. Retrieved from Holotropic Breathwork LA: https://www.holotropicbreathworkla.com/how-to-do-holotropic-breathwork

Takeda, K., & Okumura, K. (2004). CAM and NK Cells. *Evidence-based Complementary and Alternative Medicine*, 17-27.

The HeartMath Institute. (www.heartmath.org).

Vadniecorresponding, C. A., & McClung, C. A. (2017). Circadian Rhythm Disturbances in Mood Disorders: Insights into the Role of the Suprachiasmatic Nucleus. *Neural Plasticity*.

Velagapudi, R., El-Bakoush, A., Lepiarz, I., Ogunrinade, F., & Olajide, O. A. (2017). AMPK and SIRT1 activation contribute to inhibition of neuroinflammation by thymoquinone in BV2 microglia. *Mollecular and Cellular Biochemistry*, 149–162.

Wang, Q., Liu, D., Song, P., & Zou, a. M.-H. (2015). Deregulated tryptophan-kynurenine pathway is linked to inflammation, oxidative stress, and immune activation pathway in cardiovascular diseases. *Frontiers in Bioscience*, 1116–1143.

Wang, Z., Zhang, A., Zhao, B., Gan, J., Wang, G., Gao, F., . . . Edden, R. A. (2016). GABA+ levels in postmenopausal women with mild-to-moderate depression. *Medicine*, e4918.

Xie, X., Yi, W., Zhang, P., Wu, N., Yan, Q., Yang, H., . . . Ying, C. (2017). Green Tea Polyphenols, Mimicking the Effects of Dietary Restriction, Ameliorate High-Fat Diet-Induced Kidney Injury via Regulating Autophagy Flux. *Nutrients*, 497.

Ye, Q., Zhang, Q., Zheng, C., Wang, Y., & Qin, L. (2010). Casticin, a flavonoid isolated from Vitex rotundifolia, inhibits prolactin release in vivo and in vitro. *Acta Pharmacologica Sinica*, 1564–1568.

Ye, Q., Zhang, Q.-Y., Zheng, C.-j., Wang, Y., & Qin, L.-p. (2010). Casticin, a flavonoid isolated from Vitex rotundifolia, inhibits prolactin release in vivo and in vitro. *Acta Pharmacologica*.

Yogananda, P. (1946). *Autobiography of a Yogi.* New York: The Philosophical Library.

Made in United States
Troutdale, OR
10/07/2024

23486409R00127